Praise for *The Imp*

"*The Impudent Edda* gives us v
mythology from the mind of a Bos
you need to know about Odin's obsession with dick pics, Thor's
flamethrower, and Frey's gay bar experience – what's not to like!?"
—Tommy Kuusela, editor of
Folk Belief and Traditions of the Supernatural
and co-host of the *När man talar om trollen* podcast

"In this weird and wild, bawdy and beautiful mashup, the
exploits of gods and heroes are, like, wicked local. Thor waits
in line at the RMV to renew his driver's license (and also begets
Fenway Park's Wally the Green Monster and trashes a Dunkin'
Donuts). A drunken Odin is tossed from The Dropkick Murphys'
McGreevey's pub in the Back Bay. Loki goes apple picking in
his Ford Pinto. Belichick the Bold (god of strategy) beseeches
Odin and Co. to lift Tom Brady's suspension. Loki and Thor get
trapped like Charlie on the Green Line for eternity. Did I mention
MIT, Asgard, elves, Malden, valkyries, trolls, and Jörmungandr,
the sea serpent, destroying Revere Beach? The result is a raunchy
retelling of myths from the viking world, set on a collision course
with Boston lore and legend. Pissah!"
—Ethan Gilsdorf, author of *Fantasy Freaks and Gaming Geeks*

"A vital translation, regardless whether you're a Bostonian,
Asgardian or, dear god, from Connecticut."
—Chris Monks, editor of *McSweeney's Internet Tendency*

"You've heard of two renowned Eddas, *The Prose Edda* and *The
Poetic Edda*, but have you heard of *The Impudent Edda*? What? You
have not heard of the Edda found in the deepest, darkest depths
of a seedy alleyway in Boston? Blasphemy! This is a comical take
on Norse mythology and unlike anything I've read in relation to
mythology in general."
—Cassidee Lanstra, *FanFiAddict*

"A thunder's-drive through the mythos as known, found in a *wod*-induced rant on a phone-recording, as if the gods themselves were trying to remember what happened the previous night before Muninn flew the coop. With humor and profanity, and a touch of desperation, stories known and unknown are raced through like there's a giant on their eagle-tail. All reverence is shoved aside in a spilling of wisdom not unlike Kvasir having a nose-bleed. Such impudence is surely a sign of religious maturity."

—Math Jones, poet and author of
The Knotsman and *Sabrina Bridge*

"You don't have to be a Bostonian to find *The Impudent Edda* hilarious, and even if you know a lot about Old Norse mythology, you'll find its unique take both thought-provoking and insightful. The Norse gods as you've never seen them before!"

—Carolyne Larrington, translator of *The Poetic Edda* and
author of *The Norse Myths That Shape the Way We Think*

"Hilarious, ridiculous, deadpan, replete with extensive footnotes and photographs of New England locations where this stuff went down, *The Impudent Edda* is the weirdest version of Norse mythology you'll ever read. But what's weirdest of all is the fact that it's genuinely educational, and proof that a flight of fancy can be meticulously researched. A foul-mouthed joy."

—Tony Williams, author of *Nutcase* and *Cole the Magnificent*

"Thank Odin that Geirsson got this thing published before some asshole tried to explain the Norse gods away as if they were all just wizards from New York."

—Gregory Amato, author of the *Spear of the Gods* trilogy

"The text throughout is caustic, demotic and profanity-laden, as though our narrator isn't some hoary-bearded, gimlet-eyed Scandinavian bard sitting by the fireside but just an ordinary guy shooting the breeze with his buddies over a beer on the back porch. The result: a smart, lovingly rendered blend of scholarship and pastiche."

—James Lovegrove, *Financial Times*

"Previously available only in the original Bostonian (spoken by few outside of Midgard's 02127 zip code), Geirsson's translation of *The Impudent Edda* into American English is the fulfillment of his erudition, scholarship, and employment of a few thousand 'R's. While the original transcription of the *Codex Bostonia* preserved its linguistic inventiveness and visceral vulgarity, this new translation will bring these charming stories of testicle yanking, head severing, eyeball gouging, and driver's license renewing to a wider audience thanks to the translator's Odinic knowledge of the source material and his ludic fluency with the anonymous native poet's pants-drunk barbaric yawping."

—Corwin Ericson, author of *Swell* and *Checked Out OK*

"Start with a deeply layered set of myths. Invite the best storyteller you know in the greater Boston area. Add alcohol (even more than the myths already contain), and you get *The Impudent Edda*. Geirsson combines deep knowledge of Norse mythology and a skeptical irreverence for its norms (and norns), building a world of Chevy-driving, street-brawling, and bar-crawling Massachus-Æsir that remains delightfully familiar to fans of the vikings and their tales."

—John Sexton, Professor of English at Bridgewater State University and co-host of the *Saga Thing* podcast

"An anonymous poet (I like to call him Snorri Gaiman McNulty) walks into a Boston dive bar and starts rambling. Geirsson is behind the counter serving pints of Sam Adams with Brennivín chasers – taking it all in. The end product is *The Impudent Edda*: rancid, hilarious, true to the essence of Old Norse mythology (i.e., sex, deception, violence, and getting out of a tight spot by whatever means necessary). This work of scholarly rigor contains new orally-derived versions of all the myths we know and love and some that we wished we'd known earlier."

—Simon "Troll Expert" Nygaard, Assistant Professor of Old Norse religion at Aarhus University & vocalist and drummer of Wulfaz

"In the vernacular of a California-bred beach kid (insert Jeff Spicoli voice here): 'No way. *The Impudent Edda* was fuckin' awesome!' From start to finish, it is a very entertaining and clever read that brings Norse mythology to life in all of its color, and then some. I enjoyed it immensely, even if I am a Lakers fan who seriously dislikes Larry Bird and that whole Celtics team."

—Eric Schumacher, author of *Hakon's Saga* and *Olaf's Saga*

"Some stories demand to be told. These stories demand to be drunkenly shouted into the ear of an unwilling participant over the noise of a crowded bar...*The Impudent Edda* is a must-read for anyone with an interest in the humanity and hilarity of the Norse pantheon."

—Brenna Byrd, Associate Professor of German Studies and instructor in Old Norse at University of Kentucky

"*The Impudent Edda* is great fun and clearly rooted in a solid knowledge of its source material. Or maybe it really is what it purports to be: a newly discovered Edda with new information about the physics behind Loki's ability to be shagged by a horse."

—Roderick Dale, author of *The Myths and Realities of the Viking Berserkr* and co-author of *Vikings: Raids. Culture. Legacy.*

"An artistic masterpiece that reveals the deep lore of Vinland's misty shores. The primal drone of ancient wisdom from the realm where Buliwyf fought the Wendol, Leif Eriksson erected the Newport Tower, and a band of Norwegians and Goths carved the Kensington Runestone reverberates through these stories. In *The Impudent Edda*, the modern reader is presented with a string of narratives and facts about the Old Norse gods in a tradition that has clearly developed on its own but betrays its origins in the medieval Icelandic sources with details fitting as tightly as the leggings on Mr. Eriksson's statue on Commonwealth Avenue. It has truly been a delight to read this work from the hand of an Eddic poet in his prime."

—Mathias Nordvig, author of *Norse Mythology for Kids*, translator of *Völuspá – The Vision of the Witch*, and host of *The Sacred Flame* podcast

PUFFIN CARCASS  DELUXE EDITION

THE IMPUDENT EDDA

THE ANONYMOUS POET of *The Impudent Edda* is (or was) a Bostonian, as well as the most knowledgeable expert on Norse mythology to have emerged in nearly a millennium. His incredibly detailed and authentic, firsthand accounts of ancient Scandinavian religious beliefs have greatly expanded the world's understanding of the subject matter. The poet may or may not now be dead; no one really knows.

ROWDY GEIRSSON is the author of *The Scandinavian Aggressors*, editor of *Norse Mythology for Bostonians*, and a recurring contributor to the American-Scandinavian Foundation's *Scandinavian Review*. His writing has also appeared in *Medieval World: Culture and Conflict* and the Sons of Norway's *Viking Magazine*. He is the world's foremost Impudent Eddic scholar and his academic research on the subject has been published at *McSweeney's Internet Tendency* since 2010. Follow him on Xitter @RGeirsson and/or on Instadamn @rowdygeirsson, or don't.

EIRIK STORESUND is an errant Old Norse philologist, host of the *Brute Norse* podcast, and author of *Love Spells and Erotic Sorcery in Norwegian Folk Magic*. He is also the editor of *The Fool's Mirror*, Midgård's only periodical dedicated to the Scandifuturist lifestyle and aesthetics. Follow him on Xitter @brutenorse and/or on Instadamn @brutenorse, or don't.

MATT SMITH is the creator of the Icelandic saga inspired graphic novel, *Barbarian Lord*. He is also the illustrator of Dark Horse's *Hellboy: The Bones of Giants* and Image Comics' *Lake of Fire*, and his illustrations have also been featured on the *Saga Thing* podcast. Follow him on Xitter @BarbarianLord and/or on Instadamn @barbarianlord, or don't.

The Impudent Edda

*Translated from the Bostonian with
an Introduction, Commentary, and Notes
by* ROWDY GEIRSSON

PUFFIN CARCASS

PUFFIN CARCASS

An Imprint of Scandinavian Aggression
www.scandinavianaggression.com

Portions of this book first appeared online at *McSweeney's Internet Tendency* and
in print in *Norse Mythology for Bostonians* in slightly different forms.

Lyrics from *Song to Hall Up High*, words and music by Thomas Börje Forsberg,
Copyright © 1990. All rights reserved.

Lyrics from *Dirty Water*, words and music by Edward C. Cobb,
Copyright © 1965. All rights reserved.

Manufacturing via IngramSpark
Book design by Rowdy Geirsson

Library of Congress Cataloging-in-Publication Data

Names: Geirsson, Rowdy
Title: The Impudent Edda
Description: First Edition | Norumbega: Scandinavian Aggression
Subjects: Mythology, Norse, Edda, Scandinavia, Vikings,
Boston, Massachusetts, New England, Impudence.

ISBN: 979-8-218-19285-3

Puffin Carcass
An imprint of
Scandinavian Aggression
Norumbega, Vinland
www.scandinavianaggression.com

"I know you watch over me
Father of all the past
And all that will ever be
You are the first and the last

The watcher of all that lives
The guardian of all that died

The one-eyed god way up high
Who rules my world and the sky

Northern wind take my song up high
To the hall of glory in the sky
So its gates shall greet me open wide
When my time has come to die"

—Quorthon / Bathory,
Song to Hall Up High

"I'm gonna tell you a story
I'm gonna tell you about my town
I'm gonna tell you a big fat story, baby
It's all about my town

Yeah, down by the river
Down by the banks of the river, the Charles
That's where you'll find me
Along with the lovers, muggers, and thieves

Well, I love that dirty water
Oh, Boston, you're my home"

—Larry Tamblyn / The Standells,
Dirty Water

Contents

Contents

*Asterisks indicate myths that are wholly unique to
The Impudent Edda and not corroborated by earlier sources

In loving memory of good King Gylfi
Master of Disguise, Consort of Gefion, & Proselytizer of Svitjod

Foreword

It was a day much like any other. Or so it seemed. That wyrdful afternoon when I first laid eyes on the "Bostonian transcription."

I had just returned to my office, stepping off a red-eye flight from Nunavut where I had invited myself to be keynote speaker and toastmaster for the International Saga Conference. My cupbearer, whom I affectionately named Snot-Nose (after his enduring sinus infection) had been kind enough to chauffeur my 1968 model Trolls Royce to Fort Christina International Airport in New Sweden, New Jersey. Being in a rush, I dropped him off at the bus stop so he wouldn't muck up the passenger seat and promptly headed to the office.

My secretary was nowhere to be seen, and I remember finding it rather irksome. I sat down and waited for her in the dark, letting my annoyance fester through the wee hours until dawn. When she finally arrived and switched on the lights, she gave me the queerest of looks but did not address me verbally. I knew then that this day would drastically uproot both of our lives. Despite that, I could not have foreseen the severity.

She stared at me like there was something in my mustache— or something along those lines—and averted her eyes when I opened my mouth to speak. The tension slackened as I took her seal fur coat and instructed her to wash her hands. After careful examination of her fingernails, I kissed her good morning. She brought me my Dansko clogs and a cigarette, and I retreated to my scriptorium to work on whatever.

I mulled over her glance as I stirred my morning Fjellbekk[1] pitcher. It haunted me like an Inuit fairy tale. In my mind's eye, I simulated each and every scenario that might have prompted that look and retraced the events that had transpired the last time I had seen her.

She serves up luncheon at an auspicious hour every day. The menu varies throughout the week, according to seasonal availability and the life cycles and migratory patterns of the aquatic mammals of circumpolar regions. In hindsight, it was foolish not to realize that this was a very advantageous position for her, and a vulnerable one for me. I had let my guard down. I felt my stomach turn with a loud, ogreish grunt. Like a bear stirring annoyedly at the end of its winter-long nap. I was that bear, waking up to the asymmetry of power between us. And she was the Sámi huntsman lurking outside, waiting for me to emerge from my den. Prepared to send me to the Sáivu-realm or wherever Sámi bears go when they die. And then haul my carcass home to have the women butcher and cook me.

"Cook me?" I yowled, scratching my pelt. I began to wonder if last week's menu item, the whale sashimi, was in fact human flesh. Was that why she eyed me so queerly? With some disquietude, I questioned why she would do this to me. To make an ass out of me, no doubt. A prank, perhaps, to provoke some kind of reaction...any reaction at all. Anything to break my mask of stoic Norwegian detachment. To humiliate me.

I must admit that I had, in fact, been letting my guard down. I had grown self-satisfied and distant. Not there for her, looming over her shoulder as I should have been, scrutinizing her. I rubbed my eyes as I cried into my drink. It was turning brackish with tears. More like the Baltic than the eponymous mountain stream that the cocktail was meant to evoke.

---

[1] Fjellbekk ("Mountain creek") recipe (serves 1): • ¾ ounce aquavit • ¾ ounce vodka • ¾ ounce lime juice • Lemon-lime soda. Mix over ice and stir.

I thought about the day we first met. It was out on the Hungarian Plain. The scent of her hair, smoky and pungent. I will never forget how she laughed when I presented the wine cup I had crafted from her husband's skull that first night in my yurt.

Never have I heard a woman laugh like that. Laughing so hard the champagne slobbered down her chin. She laughed all night and the morning after. And she continued to laugh in the weeks that followed. A little too much, actually. It was blood curdling. Sometimes I could still hear her chuckling on the other side of the door.

"My sweet Ildico...do you think less of me now for eating a human being?" I thought to myself. "Even though it was you who set me up and made me pig out on the mystery meat?" Arousing divine fury just by having lunch...what would become of me now? Was I, the man-eater, less human now than before? Or was the monster inside of me all along?

I looked at myself in the mirror. That trolls dwell inside people is a fact known by all with an eye for such things. I am known to be an extraordinarily red-faced man. But the hot rush of blood squashing unrepentantly through my cardiovascular system reddened it further, giving me an oddly bonobo-like appearance with my tiny ears and slightly askew ski-jump nose. I raised my fist and shattered the mirror in atavistic rage. Seven years is a small price to pay for such a caliber of catharsis, and not all that long, anyway, as far as bad luck goes.

I was adequately pantsdrunk and about to confront her with my suspicions when she abruptly entered carrying a tray of delicious potato lefse canapés with fresh cracked pepper and ketchup—my favorite. Finding it impossible to continue on the warpath, I calmed down and allowed the treats to please and delight my senses.

I lit another cigarillo and rested my elbows on my garnet cloisonné Norway pine desk, my eyes falling like a Laestadian drape across the oil painting of Mount Himmelbjerget in Denmark. An exquisite piece: first, the peak shining in the bright, yet anemic northern midday sun. And at its base, the Dane, weeping without resolve. Bleeding from his plump knuckles, snot spouting from his nostrils. Trousers soggy with tears, dripping down his knees, and puddling in waterlogged sand. Unable to comprehend the mountain's one hundred meter summit.

I puffed on my smoke using the lefse roll as a cigarette holder as I contemplated this and many other past successes. I pondered my honorary deanship at the University of Inari. I admired the Golden Matchbook of the Arnamagnean Collections,[2] and so on. However, I could not shake the notion that knots were being tied in the web of fate, leaving a weird taste in my mouth. Almonds, perhaps?

Ildico entered again. "My king," she said and produced a fistful of documents from a narwhal skin valise. On top was a print-out of all the texts in which she had broken up with me and a formal letter of resignation.

"Written?" I chortled, having reminded her multiple times in the past that the penned word carried no weight inside those four walls. After all, people can write all sorts of nonsense. That doesn't make it true.

"Eight witnesses in good standing, as the *Lex Rugiorum* demands," I repeated and shuffled her grievances to the bottom of the pile. And there it was: the transcript of the original recording. The very first facsimile of the *Codex Bostonia* that the venerable archivist, Rowdy Geirsson, had asked me to assess. Some mangled version of which I dare assume you are now holding in your hands, whether you can actually read or not.

Great monuments cast long shadows, but like Roman aqueducts, they are soon toppled by barbarian might. Such was the sad fate of this document, which at first must have seemed doomed to a pathetic and obscure non-existence before it was supposedly recovered in a dirty Boston alleyway.

At a glance it might not seem like much, but what you are holding in your funny-looking, peculiarly proportioned hands, is

---

[2]   Symbolizing the sacred flame that consumed the Copenhagen University Library in 1728, using gold leaf extracted from the original Golden Horns of Gallehus.

the most significant philological discovery since Olof Rudbeck, in the thickets of his ideations, strayed upon the ruins of Swedish Atlantis. It is many more times significant than the Kensington Runestone and the *Simon Necronomicon* combined. More important than whatever sweet nothings Odin whispered into his son's ear that smoggy afternoon when Balder lay on the funeral pyre.

A previously unknown body of Norse myths!

It seemed rather far-fetched, at first, that the myths of the ancient Northmen should still be vivaciously passed around like an embalmed horse phallus as late as the 21st century. In New England of all places. It was once common knowledge that the Danelaw only extended as far as the Mercian border, yet here we see the intrepidly Norse disregard for British territorial integrity at its logical conclusion: the export of delinquent ultra-violence and crudely mythologized dick jokes across time and space, extending the viking diaspora's ethnocultural pastime of oath-breaking as far as the laws of nature allow. Sure enough, the discovery has seen its fair share of naysayers since the day it exposed itself to an unwitting (and usually unwilling) academic audience.

I remember when Rowdy presented his findings at the Mythology Conference in Falkenberg a while back. The keynote speaker at the event—a medievalist of high renown whose name I refuse to take in my mouth, but let's call him Sudy Rimek—physically blocked his path as he attempted to take the stage, calling his pioneering efforts "a clownish mockery" of the discipline. It was only during the coffee break when Rowdy and I cornered the professor in the men's room that we managed to force the hand of scholarly consensus by waterboarding him in the urinal.

Inspired by Viking Era discursive traditions, factions supporting the authenticity of the Boston Edda set out across the seas. They say the pen is mightier than the sword, and many a bloodied pen we carried across the campuses of distant lands. In Oxford we rounded up the Department of Anglo-Saxon, Norse and Celtic and made them watch as we smashed the statue of Ursula Dronke that they venerated with repulsive offerings of cheese and red wine. A fittingly symbolic end to the fading paradigm. Not all were as easily convinced: at the University of Lund we barricaded and torched the conference hotel when most of the attendees were either drunk or sleeping. At Freiburg they are still paying off an indulgent sum of Norumbegeld[3] to Puffin Carcass in exchange for an amnesty on German-style scholarly criticism. In summary, few of even the most Teutonically-schooled logical positivists now dare to openly oppose the authenticity of the *Codex Bostonia.*

Earlier in this expositional monologue, I mentioned my suspicions towards the written word. Oral fixation aside, this tome is but an adaptation of a far more direct source. The thing I beheld that fateful morn was a vernacular, critical transcription of the original recording in the eldritch Bostonian Tongue. Paleographically, I cannot doubt the authenticity of the transcription. The language of the original skald is "Southie" to the bone. By linguistic criteria alone, a forgery is out of the question, and this is further supported by both metadata and the informed guesswork of urban planners, social workers, and so on.

The argument forms a perfect circle. There cannot, in my opinion, be any doubt. The few closed-minded and lazy "experts" still in denial are simply trying to suppress this book because they know the dissemination of its contents would force them to question all the established truths of their frail and dying disciplines. We will get to you soon enough.

Hence, it is my supreme pleasure to hand off this most essential and iconoclastic text to every friend of the North (whichever side of the Atlantic that may be) and present to you *The Impudent Edda* for the first time in English!

—EIRIK STORESUND

---

[3] Protection money paid by institutes of higher education to prevent campus incursions by Norumbegan marauders. Norumbega is a theoretical construct pertaining to the historic lands bordering Massachusetts Bay within greater Vinland.

Introduction

The classic tales of Norse mythology have entertained men, women, and children for centuries, albeit in very different capacities and formats as time has passed and society has evolved. While stories such as Odin's belligerent murder of a greedy witch or Thor's cross-dressing misadventure with evil frost giants may have always provided a certain degree of entertainment value through the ages regardless of time period or culture, they also significantly shaped and guided the daily lives of the pre-Christian Scandinavians who originated them. These stories occupied a central role in the spiritual beliefs of the vikings, and the Northmen and women who stayed behind at home while their brethren went off plundering and colonizing overseas.[1] It was only with the gradual Christian-ization of Scandinavia during the four centuries that straddled the year 1000 that the importance of the Norse gods among the Scandinavians faded, though the stories of their lewd, immature, and occasionally heroic exploits lived on and were eventually preserved in the written word.

---

[1] It is a common, present-day misconception that all Norsemen and women were vikings. This is misleading, as only the medieval Scandinavians who sailed away from their homes to conduct raids were considered to be vikings in their own day. The proper usage of the possible assortment of words (Norse, viking, heathen, pagan, North[wo]men, Nordic, etc.) that are available to describe the raid-ers, farmers, pagan priests, Christian converts, and various other groupings of Viking Age Scandinavians continues to inspire debate among academics and other highly opinionated individuals.

"Edda" is the term that has come to be given to each of the three main sources containing the traditional stories of Norse mythology. The fantastical stories preserved in the Eddas have become increasingly popular in recent decades, especially as modern translations and technological advances have enabled them to reach larger and larger audiences. They have served as substantial sources of inspiration for many great writers, artists, and composers. Prominent figures such as Richard Wagner, Henry Wadsworth Longfellow, JRR Tolkien (and consequently most other contemporary fantasy novelists and game developers), and Quorthon (of Swedish viking metal fame) all borrowed and embellished upon the original Eddic material to bring their own creative visions to life. As a result, and thanks in particular to the global audience reached by *The Lord of the Rings* and *The Hobbit* film franchises in the 21st century, the average non-Norse person is now more familiar than ever with the iconography of Norse mythology, even if he or she is not fully aware of it.[2]

It is also important, if somewhat ironic, to note that each of the Eddas themselves was simply the culmination of a grand, oral—not written—tradition in which the stories of Odin, Thor, and all the others were passed down from generation to generation for centuries. As such, these stories certainly varied over distance as well as over time throughout the Nordic region. Thus, it is highly unlikely, for example, that the version of the story about the trickster god, Loki, tying his own hairy scrotum to a goat's beard and then playing tug of war with it was the same in Sweden around the year 900 as it was in Greenland two centuries later, if the story even existed in both places/time periods at all.

---

[2]   One familiar example for the average movie-goer is that of Smaug, the cruel and lazy dragon from *The Hobbit*, who was blatantly modeled after the dragons that appear in ancient Norse literature—right down to the hoard of gold and demonic-speaking abilities. Tolkien very deliberately based many aspects of his writings on the characters, themes, and environments found in the myths and sagas of the Northmen.

As the collective repository of most Norse mythology, the Eddas provide only a very limited window into what must have once been a much more robust and nuanced mythology than that to which we are presently afforded insight today.

In addition to the Eddas themselves, short mythological tales and references also exist in the worn pages of other medieval manuscripts. *Flateyjarbók*, the heftiest of ancient Icelandic manuscripts, contains a wealth of saga material and some mythological material, as does the *Gesto Danorum*, the ancient history of the Danes, written by Saxo Grammaticus, although in his work the gods are presented as evil-doing mortals rather than immature but divine beings. Many other manuscripts have also preserved stories that shed light on ancient Scandinavian thought and beliefs such as *Völsunga Saga* and *Hrólfs Saga Kraka*, and while these certainly help to paint a fuller picture of the known aspects of Norse mythology, they nonetheless typically focus on the earthly exploits of mortal men and women rather than those of the gods. The Eddas thus remain the main sources devoted specifically to the deeds of the gods, and in that sense they are invaluable.

The two earliest Eddas were recorded in Iceland in the 13th century and were the culmination of that country's long tradition of oral story-telling. The first of these Eddas was long thought to have been transcribed by a monk known as Saemundr Sigfusson the Wise (though now there is some contention about the authorship) and is known by many names: *The Codex Regius*, *The Saemundr Edda*, *The Eldest Edda* (formerly *The Elder Edda*), and most commonly, *The Poetic Edda*, because the bulk of its contents are written in poetic verse. The Norse people, as with most other ancient and medieval peoples, loved poetry and generally chose to relate their stories in long, complicated poetic verses for eager audiences. The more complicated and ornate the poem, the more respected the story-teller, or "skald" as Norse poets were called in their day.

The second Edda was written by Snorri Sturluson, a conniving and devious scoundrel who enjoyed a great degree of power and prosperity during his lifetime. As the most prominent landholder and politician in Iceland during the late 12th and early 13th centuries, he was prone to dreaming up traitorous schemes from the comfort of his very own private hot-spring hot tub until one day his enemies gathered at his house, broke in, and murdered him while he groveled in the basement. In addition to instigating blood feuds and pronouncing the laws of the land,[3] Snorri also collected manuscripts and wrote many of his own, including the original history of Norway.[4] However, he is best known for his Edda, appropriately enough called *Snorri's Edda*, *The Middle-Child Edda* (formerly *The Younger Edda*), and *The Prose Edda*.[5] While Snorri wrote this Edda in prose, rather than poetic format, he nonetheless referenced and borrowed many of the same verses that appear in *The Poetic Edda*. Both Eddas are preserved and on exhibit at the Árni Magnússon Institute for Icelandic Studies in Reykjavik.[6]

---

[3]   During his lifetime, Snorri was elected to serve as the Icelandic Lawspeaker twice. The role of the Lawspeaker was to officiate the proceedings of the Icelandic Althing, the oldest parliament in the world. Primary duties consisted of reciting the laws of the land and serving as an arbitrator of disputes, which frequently involved the irresponsible and reckless grazing of sheep and ruthless murders.

[4]   In addition to his Edda, Snorri is also the author of *Heimskringla*, known in English as *The History of the Kings of Norway*.

[5]   To add to the confusion, *The Prose Edda* has survived in a total of four different manuscripts, the most substantial of which is referred to as the *Codex Regius*, which is also one of the names for *The Poetic Edda*. The more common titles of *The Prose Edda* and *The Poetic Edda* (or Elder Eddas when referred to collectively), however, will be used exclusively and consistently throughout this edition of *The Impudent Edda*.

[6]   Other copies of *The Prose Edda* exist in Denmark, Sweden, and the Netherlands, but the copy in Iceland is the oldest, most complete, and most famous.

*The dank alley in South Boston where archaeologists
discovered the only extant copy of* The Impudent Edda.

The third Edda was recorded somewhat more recently during
the early 21st century, specifically on June 12, 2019, in Boston,
Massachusetts. In a drastic departure in terms of recording method
in comparison to the two earlier Icelandic Eddas, this Edda was not
hand-written in a fine, graceful script on parchment or vellum, but
rather was audibly recorded on a mobile telephone device and found
abandoned in an alleyway behind a local bar next to a puddle of
piss in the city's famously angry, Celtic neighborhood colloquially
known as "Southie." The poet remains unknown to this day, but
thanks to the remarkable preservative properties of non-biodegrad-
able digital technology, this Edda survived the damaging passage
of time and weather and has since come to be regarded—though
not without some dispute as will be discussed further below—as
the most important find relating to Norse mythology and ancient

Scandinavian spiritual beliefs since the exhumation of the Oseberg Ship in 1904-1905.[7] As with the other two Elder Eddas before it, it has taken on many names, including: *The Youngest Edda*, *The Infant(ile) Edda*, *The Wicked Retarded Edda*, *Some Dumb Masshole's Edda*, and, most commonly, *The Boston Edda* in informal contexts and *The Impudent Edda* in formal ones.

The audio device itself has come to be known as the *Codex Bostonia*, and *The Impudent Edda* simply comprises the main narrative audio file recorded on it; it is the content of this audio file that forms the foundation of the text presented in this book. The *Codex Bostonia* continues to be studied, however, and new discoveries are uncovered on a periodic basis. In particular, during the global lockdown of 2020, researchers found an additional stash of hidden audio files stored in a previously secret location on the device's memory card. This new material—quite extensive in volume—is being documented on an ongoing basis. Transcriptions of these "lost myths" are being released online for the general public as they become available.[8] And as with the Icelandic Edda manuscripts, the *Codex Bostonia* is often on exhibit itself (when not being studied by researchers) and may be viewed in all of its cracked-touch-screen splendor at the Museum of Bad Art in Somerville, Massachusetts.

As with the elder *Poetic* and *Prose Eddas*, *The Impudent Edda* was composed in the vernacular of its time and place. It does not feature the complex arrangements of wordplay and meter as found in *The Poetic Edda*, nor does it feature the tense, often direct and to-the-point styling of *The Prose Edda*. Rather,

---

[7] The Oseberg ship was exhumed in 1904-1905 in Vestfold, Norway. It was a remarkable find, containing numerous grave goods in excellent condition. The ship itself has become the basis for the world's collective imagination regarding the ideal appearance of a standard viking sea-going vessel, replete with dragon-headed prow.

[8] These "lost myths" may be accessed by visiting: *https://www.mcsweeneys.net/columns/norse-mythology-for-bostonians*.

The tales of the Norse myths have been preserved, illustrated, and re-written down for centuries. While such manuscripts have not typically contributed new mythological knowledge beyond that found in the Elder Eddas, the arrival of The Impudent Edda *has invited scholars the rare opportunity for new interpretations of some of this older material, such as this image of Odin from an 18th century Icelandic manuscript. Is Odin simply wearing ornate, old-timey garb as has long been assumed to be the case? Or did an unknown Icelandic scribe from 300 years ago accurately foretell Odin's future sports team allegiances? These questions, and others, remain open for future study.*

The Impudent Edda meanders its way through a series of loosely connected events in the days of the lives of the Norse gods in a sort of stream of consciousness that would make Massachusetts native, Jack Kerouac, proud. *The Impudent Edda* is contemporary to its time and place, just as the *Poetic* and *Prose Eddas* were to theirs.

The text presented in this volume is the first standard English language translation of *The Impudent Edda* to ever be produced. This is not, however, the first actual publication of *The Impudent Edda*, because a transcription of the text as recorded in its original Bostonian dialect was previously released in 2020. While Bostonian is a charmingly profane yet somewhat coherent derivative of English, and thus decipherable to a large swath of the English-speaking population, it does not provide for a smooth and easy reading experience for readers who come from outside of New England. This translation thus offers a newer, more accessible version of the same content for a broader audience. The nuances and complexities inherent to the translation of *The Impudent Edda* are addressed in more detail in the section of introductory material entitled, "An Editorial Note on the Translation."

In terms of the content itself, *The Impudent Edda* follows the two Elder Eddas closely in the overall mythic story arc—the creation of the world, the adolescent behavior featuring the sex-crazed and temper-tantrum-fueled trials and tribulations of the gods, and the complete and utter destruction of the world and almost everything in it by a relentless fire at the end of time. There are, however, a number of substantial deviations that occur in the actual transpiring of certain events, as well as the inclusion of a handful of episodes that occur neither in *The Poetic Edda* nor *The Prose Edda*. Similarly, those two Eddas contain certain episodes that are missing from *The Impudent Edda*. The same may be said of the other sources containing mythological material, such as the aforementioned *Flateyjarbók* or *Völsunga Saga*. All of this is to be expected given that each source is nothing more than a very narrow snapshot of the specific version of Norse mythology that

*The Kensington
Runestone.
Early evidence
of Scandinavian
involvement in
Minnesota,
or hoax?*

existed in the specific era and place in which it was recorded, with
each authors' own biases and prejudices present in the recording.
The most substantial of these discrepancies have been addressed
in the footnotes of the text of this translation.

As mentioned above, the legitimacy of *The Impudent Edda*
has been disputed, most frequently by members of the academic
establishment. Many scholars of mythology and medieval or com-
parative literature have questioned the authenticity of the Edda,
citing the inability to verify its origin, the lack of supporting
contextual archaeological material, and its inconsistencies with
the two Elder Eddas. Proponents of *The Impudent Edda*, which
include many armchair folklorists and online lifestyle gurus, conversely argue that while its legitimacy cannot be proven, neither

can it be disproven. The proponents are usually quick to point out that this is not a repeat of the Kensington Runestone incident[9] and that no one is postulating that *The Impudent Edda* is an authentic medieval document that has survived the same passage of time as the Elder Eddas. Experts all agree that *The Impudent Edda* is multiple centuries younger and that it was recorded in a time and place quite different from those of the Elder Eddas.

Additionally, and as was mentioned at the beginning of this Introduction, Norse pagan beliefs certainly dwindled drastically with the conversion to Christianity in Scandinavia, but there is reason to believe that they may have never been stamped out completely. Small numbers of Scandinavians continued to worship Thor, Odin, and Frey's enormous penis in secret long after the coming of Christianity to the Nordic region. This is particularly well-documented in the case of Iceland,[10] but it is also believed to be true of the other Scandinavian countries as well. The extent to which these pagan customs continued to be practiced is unknown, but it remains entirely plausible that the stories and beliefs of the old gods may have evolved over that course of time and eventually made their way to Boston via Worcester, Massachusetts, which was a major destination for Swedish immigrants in the 19th century.

---

[9] The Kensington Runestone incident was initiated in 1898 when farmer Olof Ohman discovered what he claimed to be an original Norse runestone in Douglas County, Minnesota dating to the 14th century. The stone has been studied and its authenticity debated ever since. The majority of the scholarly community generally considers it to be a hoax because linguistic analysis has revealed that the language carved into the surface of the stone is not identical to the familiar Old Swedish as is found in other, contemporaneous artifacts from the old country, but the verdict remains inconclusive.

[10] In the year 1000, Iceland voted to become a Christian nation but continued to allow the worship of the pagan gods among its populace provided that such practice only occurred in the privacy of the home.

Furthermore, much like wicca, Ásatrú[11] has been on the rise now for decades, with believers of the old ways coming out of the dark in increasing numbers. Ásatrú's presence in New England is not documented in the historical record prior to the loosening of social norms that occurred during the latter half of the 20th century, and the question remains as to whether the beliefs and customs associated with the pagan religion were ever present in the Commonwealth prior to the cultural revolution or not. Is *The Impudent Edda* the first instance of Ásatrú beliefs found in Massachusetts, long kept secret, to have emerged from the prevailing Anglo-Saxon Protestant and Irish/Italian Catholic shadows into the light of day? Do the stories that it contains provide genuine evidence of a more evolved, heretofore unknown version of Norse mythology than was previously preserved in medieval Iceland? Or is it all just complete bullshit?

The debate continues, unresolved. The purpose of this translation is not to argue the case one way or the other, but rather to provide the general public with access to material that has never before been available in an easy-to-read format. The Elder Eddas have been available to the general English-speaking public in various translations for decades, and now for the first time ever, *The Impudent Edda* joins their ranks. The reader is invited to come to his or her own conclusion.

---

[11] Ásatrú is a present-day pagan religion that revolves around the Norse gods, including customs reminiscent of ancient Norse pagan rituals, minus, of course, the elements of human and animal sacrificial slaughter.

An Editorial Note on the Translation

As mentioned in the Introduction, *The Impudent Edda* was originally preserved as an oral recording on a lost and forgotten smartphone now known simply as the *Codex Bostonia*. Because the Edda was recorded in this manner rather than the more commonly employed written word, it becomes an impossible task for the listener to overlook the distinct vernacular inherent to its locality: the Boston dialect of contemporary American English. This particularity has lent *The Impudent Edda* its own unique flavor and imbued it with a certain richness of wordplay not found in either of the Elder Eddas. It has also lent the task of translating *The Impudent Edda* into standard modern English its own distinct set of challenges.

The anonymous poet of *The Impudent Edda* orated his Edda with a thick accent that is generally difficult to comprehend for the untrained ear. The pronunciation of the vast majority of words that the poet speaks during the course of his telling of the Edda is, to put it quite frankly, utterly wrong by any modern English language standards (regardless whether such standards are American, British, Australian, Canadian, etc.).

Perhaps the most noticeable aspect of the poet's flagrant deviation from accepted spoken word standards is his tendency to completely eliminate the sound of the letter "r" in a very high proportion of words. His vowels generally sound garbled and butchered, which, combined with his crude and harsh pronunciation of the consonants, results in an overall audible effect that essentially embodies the polar opposite of the soft, sing-songy cadence of the spoken Scandinavian languages (Danish excluded).

Because this volume is a translation from the poet's Bostonian to actual English, standard English spellings have been used throughout. While this is doubtless a much-needed corrective strategy, it also diminishes the special nuances and character of the original recording. A significant sense of intonation is dramatically lost, and simply put—even if only mentally inflected—this translation just doesn't *sound* the same as the original recording (although the transcription previously mentioned in the Introduction remains faithful to the poet's intended vision).

For a comparison of the differences between the transcription and the translation, consider the two following renditions of a passage taken from the myth entitled *Odin Commits Suicide* that appears in both volumes.

From the transcription released in 2020:

"N' then as if that wasn't hahdco'ah r'enough, he goes n' he hangs himself with a noose from Yggdrasil n' so now his dead body's just danglin' there, his neck stretched longah r'en a fuckin' python n' he's got a goddamned spee'ah stickin' outtah his abdomen."

From the present translation:

"And then as if that wasn't hardcore enough, he goes and he hangs himself with a noose from Yggdrasil, and so now his dead body's just dangling there, his neck stretched longer than a fucking python, and he's got a goddamned speer sticking out of his abdomen."

Clearly, the translation loses some of the special flair inherent to the *Codex Bostonia*'s original recording and its faithful transcription, but gains a greatly enhanced degree of comprehensibility for the general public. Such is the cost of all translations everywhere.

Additionally, the anonymous poet of *The Impudent Edda* employed many archaic colloquialisms unique to his specific milieu of early 21st century Boston. Such linguistic flights of fancy are consistent with the Elder Eddas; each relies on the language of its own time and place to relay its own version of the perverted and over-the-top tales that comprise the mythology. It is thus the translator's task to decipher and render the original manuscript (hand-written or voice-recorded) accessible to the average reader. To that end, many of the most localized colloquialisms present in *The Impudent Edda* have been rendered more generically for ease of reading comprehension for the broader public. An example from the myth entitled *Cosmological Frost Giant Genocide* follows for comparison (with the relevant alteration highlighted in bold font):

From the transcription released in 2020:

"N' right next tah this intahstellah gallows tree was a massive black hole called Ginnungagap that swallowed evuhrything up like it thought it was **the budget fahr the Big fuckin' Dig'ah somethin'** n' then on each side'ah it were a couple'ah sehrious shit holes."

From the present translation:

"And right next to this interstellar gallows tree was a massive black hole called Ginnungagap that swallowed everything up like it thought it was **the national fucking deficit or something,** and then on each side of it were a couple of serious shit holes."

In addition to correcting the rampant and pervasive abuses of the English language, the translation provided in this example also substitutes the original reference to the "Big Dig" with a reference to the "national deficit" instead. This is because the Big Dig is unique to Boston; it is the label applied to the city's excessively over-budget and ridiculously prolonged civil works project that relocated its elevated freeways to subterranean tunnels during the 1980s, 1990s, and 2000s. While anyone familiar with Boston will likely understand the reference, it cannot be assumed that many readers hailing from beyond Massachusetts will recognize it. Thus, it has been replaced with a reference to a much more broadly understood topic that conveys the same basic purpose and meaning in the context of the Edda—the national deficit. Similar substitutions have been made throughout the translation to improve the flow of the text where possible to do so without compromising the intended meaning.

However, references that are crucial to the actual meaning of the text, such as those pertaining to specific locales as well as individuals of special local significance, have been maintained and simply commented upon in the footnotes as necessary.[1] Thus, just as the Impudent Eddic poet intended, Revere Beach remains the place where the gods created the first crappy, waterlogged forms of human life, Balder remains known as Brady, etc.

Additionally, *The Impudent Edda* contains many asides and outbursts throughout the entirety of its recording that deviate from the telling of the actual myths themselves, such as that which occurs mid-way through the story about Odin excreting mead while flying through the sky after having shape-shifted into the form of an eagle:

---

[1]   In the case of archaic Scandinavian words relating to the Norse cosmos and mythological ongoings, this translation has employed standard English spellings in the text because they are already familiar to most readers. Such spellings also most closely match the utterances of the anonymous poet himself as recorded on the *Codex Bostonia*. Thus, Odin instead of Óðinn, Yggdrasil instead of Yggdrasill, etc. In the introductory material and footnotes found throughout this volume, the spellings for textual sources have maintained their ancient forms. Thus, *Völuspá* instead of *Voluspa*, *Völsunga Saga* instead of *The Saga of the Volsungs*, etc.

"Come on, Tuuka!
This is fucking bullshit for fuck's sake!"

This sort of extraneous material (which generally pertains to the on-ice performance of the Boston Bruins that the poet presumably watched while orating his Edda) has been edited out of this edition because it was deemed completely irrelevant.

The overall intent and hope with this translation is to preserve the spirit and voice of the original recording to the highest degree possible while making it accessible to a general readership (ages 18 and up). Nonetheless, no Edda can be completely separated from the context of its time and place, and nor should it be.

You can take the Edda out of Boston, but you can't take Boston out of the Edda.

Old Norse Astrophysics

The northern gods inhabit a universe held together by a very different set of astrophysical properties than those that inform our most commonly accepted collective understanding of the cosmos. The gap[1] between these two schools of thought is so incredibly vast that they are essentially irreconcilable, and while one need not possess full comprehension of each and every astrophysical property that courses through the Norse myths, a fundamental grasp of the conceptual framework is useful to properly appreciate them. A brief overview is therefore provided here in modern scientific parlance for the casual contemporary reader.

Rather than an expanding and accelerating universe that consists of all space, time, matter, and energy and that was itself formed in the wake of a particularly forceful singularity at the beginning of all time, the Old Norse concept of the universe consists of a constant single, high-energy interstellar structure that has always been and always will be.[2] Known as Yggdrasil, this interstellar structure ex-

---

[1] A rhetorical gap, not to be confused with the Ginnungagap, which is addressed in the first myth of the main text, *Cosmological Frost Giant Genocide*.

[2] There is some debate and ambiguity surrounding the eternal nature of Yggdrasil as asserted by the Eddas. In *Völuspá*, the opening poem of *The Poetic Edda*, an unsubstantiated claim is made that Yggdrasil, in the earliest era of the universe's existence, was in fact formed from a forceful gravitational singularity, much like the Big Bang, resulting in an ash seedling bursting forth into mature, wooden splendor from the ripened black hole in which

hibits a visible electromagnetic spectrum that resembles the form of an enormous ash tree with three asymptotic giant branches forming its roots while numerous high-luminosity evolutionary model protoplanetary nebulae constitute the likeness of its leafy limbs. Instances of large-scale gamma radiation have been observed at Yggdrasil's extremities, particularly at one of its asymptotic giant branches where a single long-duration gamma-ray burst known as Níðhöggr the Dragon augments the cosmic radioactive decay rate by nibbling upon it at the molecular level.

Yggdrasil's branch-like protoplanetary nebulae are afflicted by high-order magnitude sub-pockets of interstellar dust and gas within four distinct high-latitude diffuse molecular clouds, creating dense clump formations on its non-ionized plasmic leaves and negatively impacting Yggdrasil's coefficient of photosynthesis. Within the Old Norse school of thought, these molecular clouds are known as Dáinn, Dvalinn, Duneyrr, and Duraþrór and are often depicted as four aggressive male deers ravenously chomping away at the extraterrestrial leaf-flesh of the known universe.

Also detected among Yggdrasil's protoplanetary nebulae is an unnamed binary neutron star system, the hostile pulsar of which emits highly magnetized electromagnetic radiation which is transmitted as a series of avian insults via a squirrel-like forbidden mechanism known as Ratatosk that undergoes a spontaneous spin-flip transition, free-falling at the speed of light and restabilizing among Yggdrasil's asymptotic giant branches where the radioactive avian insults are absorbed by Níðhöggr the Dragon, resulting in a sharp upward spike of the Dragon's already highly excited state. Níðhöggr reacts to this increase of energy through a series of rapid-inimical non-thermal ophidian invectives that are redshifted towards Ratatosk and re-transmitted through the

---

it was planted. The *Prose* and *Impudent Eddas* do not corroborate this, and the notes throughout the text of this volume take the stance that Yggdrasil is considered truly eternal in Old Norse thought.

Friedrich Wilhelm Heine's classic 1886 illustration of the high-energy interstellar structure known as Yggdrasil.

spectral line to the unnamed hostile pulsar. This antagonistic interstellar exchange of energy continues for all eternity, even after the rest of the universe is destroyed in the catastrophic cosmic fire of one final, massive supernova explosion known as Ragnarök.

A Brief Overview of the 9 Worlds

Within the Old Norse school of astrophysical thought, nine primary life-supporting atmospheric systems are believed to exist within the interstellar structure of Yggdrasil's ash tree-like framework. Each system possesses its own unique characteristics and serves as host to its own uniquely evolved, native species of lifeforms. The 9 Worlds as they were known among the ancient Norse are as follows:

Asgard: Home to the primary tribe of gods known as the Aesir, Asgard is located on the luminous spectrum of the uppermost of Yggdrasil's three asymptotic giant branches. Essentially a fortress, Asgard is surrounded by massive, stone walls to keep its enemies out. Within the protection of these walls may be found the individual halls and hang-out places of the gods, such as Valhalla (Odin's hall of the slain), Fensalir (Frigg's salon in the marshy Fens), and Sökkvabekkr (where Sága seduces married gods into having extramarital affairs). Asgard is connected to Middle-Earth by Bifrost, the magnificent rainbow bridge.

Elf World: Known as Alfheim in earlier sources, Elf World is located among a different magnitude of the luminous spectrum of the same asymptotic giant branch as Asgard. As its name suggests, Elf World is home to the elves.

Dwarf World: Known as Svartelfheim in earlier sources, Dwarf World is a damp and dark place located beneath the ground of Middle-Earth.

Giant Land: Known as Jotunheim in earlier sources, Giant Land is located among the mid-level asymptotic branch of Yggdrasil, due east of Middle-Earth on the luminous scale. Giant Land is a cold and forbidding place full of mountains. As its name suggests, it is the home of frost giants and mountain giants, but not fire giants.

Hel: The grim, gray land of the dead that awaits those who do not die in battle and is presided over by the demoness with the same name, Hel. Located near, or within, Niflheim along the third and lowest asymptotic branch of Yggdrasil.

Middle-Earth: Also known as Midgard, Middle-Earth is located among the mid-level giant asymptotic branch of Yggdrasil and is the home of humans. Encircled by a vast ocean, Middle-Earth is nonetheless connected to Asgard by Bifrost, the rainbow bridge.

Muspellsheim: The land of fire and home of fire giants, it is unclear exactly where Muspellsheim is located within Yggdrasil's interstellar structure, but it is a hot and evil place. The heat from Muspellsheim melted the ice of Niflheim from which all life in the universe subsequently arose.

Niflheim: A dark, misty world of ice and cold, Niflheim is located along the luminous spectrum of Yggdrasil's lowest asymptotic branch. Once devoid of life, it is now populated by Hel and her army of undead zombies. Niflheim is located in dangerously close proximity to the radioactive decay emanating from the long-duration gamma-ray burst known as Níðhöggr the Dragon.

Vanaheim: Home to the secondary tribe of gods known as the Vanir, Vanaheim, like Asgard, is located along the luminous spectrum of Yggdrasil's uppermost asymptotic branch.

OTHER PLACES OF INTEREST

Folkvangr: Freyja's flowery meadow located in Asgard where she receives her share of fallen warriors as delivered by the valkyries.

Ginnungagap: The primordial abyss that was located somewhere along the luminous spectrum of Yggdrasil's mid-level asymptotic giant branch at a magnitude between those of Niflheim and Muspellsheim.

Hvergelmir: Located beneath Niflheim, Hvergelmir is the spring source of all water throughout the cosmos and home to numerous, nasty snakes.

Iron Wood: Also known as Járnviðr, Iron Wood lies somewhere east of Middle-Earth and is presided over by Angrboda, mother of the notorious monsters Fenrir, Jörmundgandr, and Hel, as well as many wolves. The forest is also populated by many evil troll women.

Valhalla: Odin's hall of the slain, Valhalla is located within the protected fortress walls of Asgard. It is a magnificent hall with five hundred and forty doors and a roof constructed of shields. At Valhalla, the Einherjar, Odin's fallen warriors, battle all day and feast all night, being served roast pork and fresh mead that flows freely from the udders of Heidrun, the magical mead-bearing goat. The Einherjar are waited upon by the very same valkyries who plucked them up off the battlefield.

Well of Mimir: Beneath Giant Land is the Well of Mimir, where Odin sometimes consults Mimir's decapitated head for advice.

Well of Urd: Located in the same luminous spectrum as Asgard is the Well of Urd, where the norns live, weaving the fate of all men and women.

Old Norse Racial Diversity

Having been populated almost entirely (if not fully) with nothing but pale, white people, medieval Scandinavia was not a very racially diverse place. However, the Scandinavians have always displayed a heightened degree of social awareness, and, thus, they attempted to amend this deficiency in heterogeneity by populating their mythology with a whole array of unique races. An overview of those races is presented here, complete with all the enduring generalizations, insensitivities, and basic prejudices that one would fully expect to course through any such present-day discussion about a topic so timeless that it continues to incite and divide *Homo sapiens* even in the 21st century.

Dwarves: The dwarves are small, near-sighted creatures who live below ground in Dwarf World where they hoard gold and make magnificent jewelry. Sometimes referred to as dark-elves or black-elves, the dwarves are human-like in appearance, but much shorter, stockier, hairier, and uglier. Originally existing as maggots who burrowed under the skin of the primordial giant Ymir's cold, lifeless body, the dwarves were given human intelligence and their present physical form by Odin in one of his rare acts of sympathy and kindness.

Elves: The elves, sometimes called light-elves, are mystical, god-like beings, fair, tall, and pleasant in all ways. They possess magical abilities and live in Elf World but do not play a prominent role in *The Impudent Edda* or either of the Elder Eddas.

Giants: The antagonists of the gods. The giants existed before the gods and are generally considered to be a hostile race, although some giants go renegade and become friendly allies of the gods. Massively large in size, the frost giants and mountain giants live in Giant Land while their even more evil brethren, the fire giants, live in Muspellsheim.

Gods and **Goddesses**: The protagonists of Norse mythology. The gods and goddesses are grim, fatalistic, sex-crazed, manipulative, and immature. Most of them are classified into one of two tribes:

> **Aesir**: The Aesir comprise the primary tribe of gods and goddesses, with a broad fixation on war, death, battle, poetry, and heavy drinking. Odin and Thor belong to this tribe of gods. The Aesir live in Asgard.

> **Vanir**: The Vanir are the secondary tribe of gods and goddesses, with a fixation on sex and extreme physical attractiveness. Frey and Freyja belong to this tribe of gods. The Vanir live in Vanaheim.

In addition to the Aesir and Vanir, a handful of ambiguously divine beings also exist; their affiliations, as well as their genetics, are unknown. These figures skim a fine line between the gods and giants, frequently with mixed parentage from both races.

Norns: The norns are the weavers of fate who live beside the Well of Urd. There are three norns who have achieved superstar celebrity status: Urd (who shares the same name as the well that she lives beside), Verdandi, and Skuld, though there are many other norns, some of which are sweet and some of which are just downright ill-tempered and nasty.

Ogres: See trolls.

Trolls: A generic, catch-all term for ambiguous, off-putting, and hostile beings that do not at first glance obviously belong to the race of giants. Trolls have a tendency to live far away from all forms of civilization, usually in forests or caves. Ogres may be seen as a species subset within the genus of troll.

Valkyries: Choosers of the slain, the valkyries ride through the sky, plucking up fallen warriors on the battlefield to be taken either to Odin's hall of battle and glory, Valhalla, or to Freyja's flowery meadow, Folkvangr.

Prominent Figures of the
Old Norse Pantheon

GODS AND GODDESSES: AESIR

Balder: See Brady.

Belichick: Known as Hermod in earlier sources, little is known of Belichick's personality other than that he is very bold and a great strategical thinker. A bastard son of Odin, his mother is unknown but is presumed to not be Frigg, Odin's wife.

Brady: Known as Balder and nicknamed the White or the Beautiful in earlier sources, Brady is the most attractive of the gods, as well as the most popular ever since he started playing quarterback for the New England Patriots. Brady is the one legitimate son of Odin and Frigg and is married to Gisele,[1] known as Nanna in earlier sources, with whom he fathered Forseti, a minor god who is reputed to be good at resolving legal disputes. Forseti receives passing mention in earlier sources but does not figure into *The Impudent Edda*.

---

[1] The concept of the space time continuum in Eddic lore has always been a very fluid one. Therefore, it should come as no surprise that the poet of *The Impudent Edda* presupposed an eternal marriage between Brady and Gisele that simultaneously precluded (on a spiritual level) any possible divorce proceedings that might or might not have occurred in late 2022.

Frigg: Considered to be particularly splendid in numerous ways that go unspecified, Frigg is foremost among the goddesses. Wife to Odin and mother to Brady/Balder, Frigg nonetheless lives apart in her own home in the fens, Fensalir, because no one can tolerate living with Odin 24/7, not even an all-powerful goddess.

Gisele: Known as Nanna in earlier sources, little is known about Gisele other than that she stems from German Brazilian heritage and that she previously made a living stunning onlookers with her amazing physique as she walked up and down the catwalk. In Eddic lore, she is presented as eternally faithful and forever married to all-star quarterback/golden god Brady/Balder. She mothered Forseti, their otherwise non-descript lawyer son. See Footnote 1 on opposite page.

Hermod: See Belichick.

Hod: The blind god, a son of Odin and brother of Brady/Balder. It is uncertain who his mother is.

Hoenir: A lesser god in the Norse pantheon, Hoenir is known for being thick-skulled and none too bright. Sometimes he hangs out with Odin.

Idunn: Goddess and keeper of the magical apples of youth, which the gods and goddesses must feed upon from time to time in order to stave off old age and thereby cheat death by natural causes. Idunn is married to Bragi, the most poetic of the gods with the possible exception of Odin. Bragi is a great story-teller but goes unmentioned in *The Impudent Edda*.

Mimir: A very wise god with a traumatically short life span.

Nanna: See Gisele.

Odin: The top dog of all the gods, also known as the All-Father for his fathering of all the world. Odin's wife is Frigg, with whom he fathered Brady/Balder. As a manipulative and unfaithful husband, Odin has also fathered many other bastard sons. One-eyed, wise, war-mongering, and grim, Odin has a penchant for poetry and enjoys instigating conflicts and wandering Middle-Earth disguised as a hobo. A pair of gossiping ravens keep him company upon his throne, Hlidskjalf, from whence he watches over all the world with his all-seeing eye. In the evenings he entertains his army of undead viking warriors in Valhalla with eternal battle, roast pork, and mead that flows freely from the magical udders of the divine goat, Heidrun.

Sága: The goddess who lives at Sökkvabekkr. She enjoys drinking and flirting with Odin and/or Thor (depending on the source).

Sif: A goddess with lovely, flowing golden hair. Sif is married to Thor, and together they begat Thrud, their daughter. From an earlier relationship during her reckless youth, Sif also became mother to Ull, a highly skilled skier and archer, but who does not figure into *The Impudent Edda*.

Sigyn: The wife of Loki who presumably fell in love with him when she was very young and extremely foolish. Not much is known about Sigyn other than the role that she plays in the final days of the gods leading up to Ragnarök.

Thor: Son of Odin and Mother Earth, Thor is the strongest of all the gods. Boisterous and red-headed with a bushy beard, Thor can outdrink any other god and is proud of it. He routinely defends Asgard, the home of the gods, from the hostilities of evil giants with his mighty hammer, Mjölnir. Thor also enjoys journeying among the 9 Worlds, particularly with Loki for no apparent reason, and his hot temper often lands him in embarrassing situations. Thor is husband to golden-haired Sif, with whom he fathered their daughter Thrud. Through various extramarital affairs, he has also fathered Magni and Modi, two strapping young lads born with the strength of Thor himself. None of Thor's children play a role in *The Impudent Edda*.

Tyr: The bravest and most fearless of the gods, Tyr is a one-handed bachelor who prefers battle to diplomacy. The son of the hostile giant, Hymir and his wife Hrod, it remains unclear how Tyr became an ally and well-respected member of the gods with such disastrous lineage.

GODS AND GODDESSES: VANIR

Frey: The chief god of the weather and fertility, which is somewhat ironic since he has no children of his own. Frey is the son of Njord and the twin brother of Freyja and is married to the giantess Gerd. His most distinct feature is his enormous penis, which is almost always erect.

Freyja: Probably the sluttiest of the goddesses, Freyja suffers a bad habit of selling her body for jewelry. As with her twin brother Frey, she is also associated with fertility and is generally considered to be the hottest and most sexually desirable of all the goddesses. She also has a dark side and is somewhat death-obsessed. Like Odin, she rules over a portion of the fallen warriors who die on the battlefield from her home beside the meadow known as Folkvangr, though her role in the afterlife is much less prominent. She is the daughter of Njord and the wife of Odr, who left her to go on travels while she stayed behind and cried tears of red gold. Prior to his departure, Odr and Freyja had a beautiful daughter, Hnoss, but neither Hnoss nor Odr receive mention in *The Impudent Edda*.

Kvasir: A divine being created from the spittle of the other gods, Kvasir is also, confusingly, regarded as the wisest of the Vanir.

Njord: God of the sea and wind, Njord is married to the mountain giantess Skadi, though they live apart. Through a previous incestuous relationship with his unnamed sister, Njord is father to the sex-object god and goddess twins, Frey and Freyja.

AMBIGUOUSLY DIVINE BEINGS OF UNKNOWN HERITAGE

Aegir: An ambiguously divine being, Aegir has been named as a giant but is often regarded as a god. He is the ruler of the seas, a magnificent host of wild underwater parties, and a mighty brewer of excellent craft beer. He is married to Rán, who enjoys drowning human seafarers but goes unmentioned in *The Impudent Edda*. Together, Aegir and Rán are parents to the waves.

Charlie: Another ambiguously divine being of unknown heritage, Charlie's lot is to ride forever on the subway system beneath the streets of Boston. His existence and role in the Norse myths is attested to only in *The Impudent Edda*.

Heimdall: The watchman of the gods, Heimdall lives near Bifrost, the rainbow bridge, where he remains on constant vigilance against any enemies that might approach the homeland of the gods. He was given birth by nine mothers and is occasionally considered to be a member of the Vanir, though his genuine affiliation remains unclear. Researchers have postulated that Heimdall's nine mothers might be the wave-daughters of the ambiguously divine duo, Aegir and Rán.

Loki: The trickster god and general all-around trouble-maker. Son of the giant, Fabauti, and his wife, Laufey, neither of whom receive mention in *The Impudent Edda*. Loki is married to Sigyn, a generally nice goddess with an unfortunately poor taste in men.

Rán: Wife of Aegir and mother of the waves, Rán enjoys using her magical net to catch seafarers and drown them.

Skirnir: A servant of Frey and thus affiliated with the Vanir but not a true member of their clan. A low-ranking pseudo-deity.

Wally the Green: The bastard son of Thor and Sága, Wally the Green spends most of his existence being struck with baseballs near Frigg's home in the Fens. Like Charlie, his existence and role in the Norse myths is attested to only in *The Impudent Edda*.

GIANTS AND GIANTESSES

Baugi: Suttung's moronic brother.

Geirrod: An asshole and father of the hideous sisters, Gjalp and Greip.

Gerd: An exceptionally sexy giantess and wife of Frey.

Gilling: A typically criminal giant who is deceived and murdered by dwarves. Father of Suttung and probably Baugi.

Gjalp: One of Geirrod's hideous daughters and sister to Greip. A distasteful and deranged individual, Gjalp has an unsavory habit of menstruating a flood of blood all over the public landscape.

Greip: One of Geirrod's hideous daughters, sister to Gjalp.

Gunnlöd: The lonely daughter of Suttung who is forced to live inside a mountain.

Hymir: Father of the one-handed god Tyr, Hymir is not nearly as brave a fisherman as Thor.

Skadi: Originally a giantess and daughter of Thjazi, Skadi transcended the traditional boundaries of the Old Norse racial divide when she married Njord. Regarded as a goddess as well as a giantess from that point onwards, Skadi is known for her love of winter and special skiing abilities.

Suttung: The son of Gilling who takes revenge on the dwarves who murdered his father. Once keeper of the famed Mead of Poetry and father to Gunnlöd.

Thjazi: An asshole and the father of Skadi, with the ability to shape-shift into an eagle.

Thrym: An especially angry asshole of a giant who steals Thor's hammer as part of a devious plot to fornicate with Freyja.

Ymir: The original primordial frost giant. After murdering him, Odin used his carcass to terraform the world.

MONSTERS

Angrboda: The chief ogress of Iron Wood, Angrboda is mother to Loki's monstrous children, Fenrir, Hel, and Jörmundgandr. She has probably also birthed many mean-spirited wolves, too.

Fenrir: Also known as Fenris or the Fenriswolf, Fenrir is the demonic talking wolf fathered by Loki and born of his shameful relationship with the evil-spirited ogress, Angrboda. Fenrir is the brother of Hel and Jörmundgandr.

Goodell: Known as Surt in earlier sources, Goodell has traditionally been regarded as a menacing and spiteful fire giant hell-bent on destroying the world, and while these qualities have been maintained, he has also taken on a much more incompetent and imbecilic character in *The Impudent Edda*.

Hel: The demon woman of the underworld that shares the same name, Hel is one of Loki's hateful children from his deviant sexual relations with the ogress, Angrboda. She is the sister of Fenrir and Jörmundgandr.

Jörmundgandr: The Middle-Earth serpent and mortal enemy of Thor, Jörmundgandr lies at the bottom of the ocean, encircling the world and biting upon his own tail. Along with Fenrir and Hel, he is one of the monstrous children of Loki and Angrboda.

Surt: See Goodell.

DWARVES

Alfregg, **Dvalin**, **Berling**, and **Grer**: The four dwarves whom Freyja whores herself out to in exchange for the special necklace known as the Brisingamen. It remains unclear whether they are affiliated with either the Hel's Valkyries or the Sons of Ivaldi biker gangs.

Fjalar and **Galar**: The pair of dwarves that craft the Mead of Poetry from the spittle and blood of a murdered demigod. As with Alfregg, Dvalin, Berling and Grer, it remains unclear whether they are affiliated with either the Hel's Valkyries or the Sons of Ivaldi biker gangs.

Hel's Valkyries: One of the two main MC Dwarf gangs r~~afted~~ criminal Dwarf World underworld. The Hel's Valky~~,~~ Gull- three special treasures of the gods: Frey's golde~~ jölnir.~~ inbursti; Odin's ring, Draupnir; and Thor's ha~~

Sons of Ivaldi: One of the two main M~~ gangs and~~ arch-rivals of the Hel's Valkyries. The ~~ldi are famed~~ for having crafted: Sif's golden ha~~ magic-shrinking~~ boat, Skíðblaðnir; and Odin's fav~~ungnir.~~

THE IMPUDENT EDDA

Cosmological Frost Giant Genocide

So way back, and I mean way fucking back, like we're talking about back before the Pilgrims even knew what a fucking May-flower even fucking was, there was nothing except this big ass world tree that was shaped like a fucking gallows pole,[1] since the vikings were a bunch of real death-obsessed motherfuckers. And right next to this interstellar gallows tree was a massive black hole called Ginnungagap that swallowed everything up like it thought it was the national fucking deficit or something, and then on each side of it were a couple of serious shit holes. One of which was called Niflheim which means "cold as fuck" in ancient fucking Norse, and the other was called Muspellsheim for who the fuck knows why.[2]

---

[1]   As identified in "Old Norse Astrophysics" in this book's intro-ductory material, Yggdrasil is the term given by the Norse to the high-energy interstellar structure that corresponds to our more modern scientific concept of the universe. The word "Yggdrasil" literally means "Gallows Pole" in Old Norse because the Norse, in addition to being "death-obsessed motherfuckers" as the anon-ymous poet so acutely observes, were also keenly aware of Odin's supernatural ability to redshift his constituent electromagnetic wavelengths and reduce their frequency particles to the giant provided that he first disperses his godsfiguration and its asymptotic branches of Yggdrasil. This is discussed in more subsequent high-energy molecular disp*Suicide.* detail in the myth entitled, *Odin Co*tration here, "Niflheim"

[2]   Contrary to the poet's confidence. While all three Eddas does not mean "cold as fuck" in C

So anyway, what I guess happened one day is that some dumb shit forgot to turn down the heat in Muspellsheim on his way out, and by the time he got back home from work, not only had the power company gone and fucking bankrupted the poor bastard with the electrical bill, but this over-heating had also melted all the ice next door in Niflheim, and so what you got now is this big slushy mess that's looking like the worst fucking mud season on record, and next thing you know, some goddamned giant emerges from out of it. And no one even knows how he got down there. Still to this day, no one knows. No one even has a fucking clue, and even the scientists over at CERN are still trying to figure it out but apparently their super special supercollider's a fucking piece of shit.

But anyway, this giant's name's Ymir, and he's a real mean prick. Seriously, he's a fucking asshole. And to make matters worse, he sweats a lot. And I mean, like a fucking shit-ton a lot. Especially whenever he's sleeping at night, which is a daily occurrence even for a fucking malicious mythological creature like Ymir. I mean, the guy drips out so much fucking sweat out of his pores that it's like a fucking torrential downpour flooding Florida, and so you can just imagine the sort of horrendous mold problems any poor bastard living down at basement level's got to deal with when that shit finally fucking recedes.

But anyway, somehow all that giant sweat, it just ends up transforming into even more frost giants, you know, like somehow that sweat just got up and mutated itself into giants on its own accord like it though was a ninja turtle or some shit, only without all the radioactive goo or Splinter[3] to teach it some sick-ass ninja

---

consistently portray Niflheim as a cold, dark place, most scholars generally agree that the word "Niflheim" involves a reference to mist rather than cold. Additionally, and while not stated specifically as such here, later inferences within *The Impudent Edda* indicate a general concurrence with the Elder Eddas of Muspellsheim as a realm of heat and fire.

3   A talking sewer rat and important spiritual sensei in 1980's American mythology.

moves. Which all in all is kind of impressive from a sort of super advanced evolutionary point of view, but at the same time it's also fucking horrible because now the world's overrun with an entire fucking tribe of inbred, oversized assholes made out of magical sweat that ain't even fucking human.

Now the thing about Ymir and all his fucking frost giant sweat children is that they all subsisted on the milk of this huge ass magical cow[4] that just so fucking—LO AND BEHOLD—also happened to emerge from out of the same fucking slushpile as Ymir did. So now this cow, she starts licking up all that fucking ice that hasn't melted yet because, I mean, she's a fucking cow, right, and so she needs her fucking salt lick, and so when she does that for long enough, she eventually licks away enough ice to free up this other guy who was also somehow fucking buried down in there.[5]

Now I got to say, I don't got a clue as to where all these guys are coming from. I mean, no one knows how they all got put down there in the first place. The whole thing's like a fucking mythological mass graveyard from before the beginning of time. One of the great mysteries of the universe and all that shit.

Anyway, so now this new guy ends up having a son who turns out to be hornier than Tiger Woods on viagra, and so as soon as he gets a chance, he goes off and he starts fucking anything that moves, which basically means that he fucks a bunch of fucking frost giants. So, of course, he ends up knocking a lot of them up, and then they all give birth to a bunch of fucking little part-god,

---

4 This primordial bovine has been identifed as Audumbla in the *Gylfaginning* section of *The Prose Edda*.

5 The "other guy" as described in *The Impudent Edda* has been identified as Buri in the Elder Eddas. Buri is not generally considered to have been an evil frost giant, but rather a likeable sort of proto-god who nonetheless fraternized and copulated with the female frost giants because there were no other options at that time, and online dating had not yet been invented to help him at least try to find a more compatible match outside of his own rather limited circle of acquaintances.

part-frost-giant bastards, one of whom is our dear friend, Odin,
who's actually a pretty sick and demented individual and who
grows up to be like the Norse god version of some crooked American president.

Now Odin, he and his brothers, they don't get along so well
with Ymir since it's like I was saying, Ymir's a total fucking prick,
and so Odin and his brothers, they go and they just fucking murder the bastard right there on the fucking spot, and they don't
even think twice about it.[6] And you know what else? They don't
even try to cover it up. Everyone knows they did it, and they're all
fucking glad that they did.

But Ymir, him being the big guy that he is, he bleeds like a
motherfucker, and so all of his blood basically drowns and kills
all those other fucking frost giants that had started out as his own
sweat except for this one guy, and this one guy ends up being the
sole progenitor for repopulating the whole wide world with more
frost giants. And I don't know how the fuck that worked without
there being some sort of other female frost giant there for him
to procreate with, but this story doesn't really make much sense,
anyway, so it's just kind of like, eh fuck it, you know?[7]

---

[6]   Odin's brothers have been identified as Vili and Ve in the
Elder Eddas. They do not figure prominently in any of the Eddas,
other than to serve as accomplices to Odin's primordial act of
murder and subsequent creation of Middle-Earth in the case of
both the *Prose* and *Impudent Eddas* (*The Poetic Edda* acquits Vili
and Ve of any guilt in this particular homicidal incident).

[7]   Here, the unknown poet of *The Impudent Edda* deviates from
The Prose Edda in his conviction that "this one guy"—Bergelmir—
is the sole surviving frost giant of the cosmological genocide; the
Gylfaginning section of *The Prose Edda* asserts that Bergelmir was
accompanied by his wife as he rowed his boat through wave after wave of blood and gore to eventual safety. *The Poetic Edda*
confirms the existence of Bergelmir in its constituent poem,
Vafþrúðnismál, but remains silent on his bodily relationship to
the desecration of Ymir's cosmic corpse.

Middle-Earth is Just an Eyelash on the Celestial Gallows Pole

All right, so now what we got is this situation where Odin's got a dead fucking giant's corpse on his hands, and it's starting to rot and stink up Yggdrasil, and so he's like, you know, "Fuck this thing, it fucking stinks. What the fuck do I do with it now? It's fucking huge and I don't even know how to dispose of it properly on account of the fact that I haven't even created any waste disposal services yet."

Because, you know, you got to remember that at this point in time, there's still no fucking earth. All that there is in the entire fucking universe at this point in time is a creepy world tree used for hanging people, a big fucking fire pit, some melting ice, a big magical cow, and Ymir's dead fucking body.[8] But Odin, he's a pretty clever guy, and so what he does is he goes and he takes Ymir's corpse, and he rips it to shreds, and then he starts using its dismembered parts to terraform the entire fucking planet.

So, for example, you got Ymir's flesh becoming the ground we walk on, and his blood becoming the seas and the lakes, and his bones becoming the mountains, and his skull becoming the sky and so on and so forth. And Odin, he's like a fucking ravished madman. He doesn't spare a single fucking part of the

---

8   This list excludes the other cosmic entities that afflict Yggdrasil as described in "Old Norse Astrophysics," but it is implicitly understood that the anonymous poet is aware of them and has simply chosen to focus on the near space region of the atmosphere at this juncture of his Edda.

dead giant's body! He uses every fucking part of the corpse even
including the eyelashes which he uses to construct a fortress to
keep the frost giants out, and this fortress, it ends up getting
called Middle-Earth for I don't know the fuck why, but Tolkien
must have thought it was pretty cool back when he started hallu-
cinating about hobbits and shit in the trenches of World War 1.

But anyway, so now Odin's done with creating Middle-Earth
and all, but the thing is, Middle-Earth, it's feeling pretty lonely because it don't got no fucking people living in it yet. So what Odin
does is he and his brothers go and they take the Blue Line out to
Wonderland[9] because they're a bunch of fucking gambling addicts,
and they want to bet on the race dogs since the track was still open
back then[10] and after they blow all their cash on the wrong fucking

---

[9]   The Blue Line is one of the lines of Boston's notorious subterranean transit system known as the T (the iconography of which
was ripped off from Stockholm). The Wonderland T-station lies
just north of Boston in the coastal city of Revere. The poet's
implication that the Blue Line (which was built by the human
residents of Middle-Earth) existed prior to the creation of the
first man and woman highlights the incongruity of Old Norse
thought regarding the space-time continuum. Many instances of
such incongruity are found throughout all of the Eddas.

[10]   Here, and throughout the story of the world's creation in
general, *The Impudent Edda* adheres more closely to the tradition
of *The Prose Edda* than that of *The Poetic Edda*, but deviates from
both (for example, *The Poetic Edda*'s *Völuspá* identifies Odin's accomplices in creating human life as Hoenir and Lodur rather than
his brothers, Vili and Ve). According to the poet of *The Impudent
Edda*, Odin and his brothers rode the Blue Line of Boston's public transportation network to the site of the former Wonderland
Greyhound Park in Revere, Massachusetts, which closed in 2010
after the state instituted a ban on greyhound racing. This depiction deviates from both of the Elder Eddas, in which, despite their
own inherent differences, the scene is consistently portrayed in a
much more naturalistic setting devoid of any urban development.
Additionally, the Elder Eddas allude to actual ash and elm trees

Revere Beach in Revere, Massachusetts, where Odin and his brothers created the very first man and woman in the world from soggy flotsam and jetsam, according to the poet of The Impudent Edda.

greyhound, they decide to go for a walk on the beach, and so there they are, walking along when they find some fucking driftwood that the tide's washed up, and they think to themselves, "Hey, you know what, these pieces of driftwood, they'd make some nice fucking people if we was to turn them into people." And so they went and they turned the driftwood into people and they put them in Middle-Earth, and the people, you know, they didn't have birth control back then, and so here we are today.

But for themselves, Odin and his brothers, they also created Asgard, you know, the fucking stronghold of the gods or what-

---

as the progenitors of the human race, rather than soggy pieces of driftwood permeated with countless noxious contaminants from Massachusetts Bay's dirty water.

ever, which also just so happens to be located pretty much right next to MIT but it's also way up high in the sky, too, which is a real mind-fuck if you think about it for too long.[11]

So now at this point, I guess I ought to tell you that Odin's brothers pretty much stop figuring into the story.[12] They were never very cool in the first place, and all they do is proceed to spend the rest of their lives just sitting around at home watching reruns on HBO and Netflix whereas Odin gets out and does things like murder people and write poetry.

But anyway, getting back to the sun and the stars and the moon and all that shit, the thing you got to realize is, it's just a bunch of poor fucking people up there running around in circles in the sky. For whatever reason, Odin, he'd get into one of his fucking moods, and he'd take it out on these poor bastards by kicking them out of Middle-Earth and putting them up in a chariot in the fucking sky to go round and round and round in fucking circles till the end of fucking time when everyone dies a horrible death in a huge fucking fire. And to make matters worse, these poor bastards, they all got these sick-ass demon wolves chasing after them the whole time, and so when the entire fucking universe finally gets destroyed at the end of time, these fucking wolves are going to swallow everything they can fucking get their mouths on, which means that both the sun and the moon are going to disappear like a jelly donut in a cop's car in the parking

[11]   The poet here seems to be conflating the home of the gods with a former, upscale Irish pub located in Cambridge, Massachusetts that shared the same name (it went out of business in the wake of the 2020 pandemic). A recurring, apparent lack of sobriety impacts certain details throughout the recording of *The Impudent Edda*.

[12]   This sentence is an example of a typical convention frequently found in Old Norse literature that rather bluntly informs the reader that certain characters have played out their roles and will not be reappearing again for the duration of the work.

lot of the nearest Dunkies.[13] But also, these wolves, their mom's a nasty fucking ogress who lives out in Iron Wood.[14]

I'm not entirely sure what the point of knowing that even fucking is.

---

[13] A colloquialism for Dunkin' Donuts, which is something of a cultural institution in Boston. *The Impudent Edda* was coincidentally recorded the same year that a misguided rebranding initiative formally removed "Donuts" from the chain's official name.

[14] *The Impudent Edda*'s explanation of the Solar System, near-space atmosphere, seasons, and general passage of time is much abbreviated in comparison to the Elder Eddas but closely correlated. In each of the three Eddas, the description of the Old Norse astrophysical framework introduces advanced archaic complexities relating to these concepts. While it is not necessary to fully delve into each and every near-space aberration, the general relationship between the sun and the earth serves as a good, basic example to help illustrate the conceptual incongruities for the reader. As anyone with a basic elementary-level education knows, the sun is a G-type main-sequence star that burns brightly at the center of our Solar System while the earth orbits around it, along with the eight or nine other planetary bodies that comprise the Solar System (depending on whether one agrees or disagrees with the International Astronomical Union's declassification of Pluto as a planet or not). However, according to the ancient Norse system, the earth does not orbit the sun nor does it rotate about its polar axis as explained by the laws of gravitational force. Norse astrophysics quite simply does not even consider earth to be a planet at all (the entire concept being completely foreign) but rather a quasi-dimensional moment in the space-time continuum of the great interstellar world tree structure, Yggdrasil. And as for the sun, it is chased across the sky by a cold-hearted space wolf that ruthlessly attempts to eat it each and every day since wolves have always been known since time immemorial to be very vicious and hungry animals.

The Original Gandalf was a Maggot

So now about this time, Odin's finally getting to feeling like he's about done with his world-creating frenzy, but then he realizes there's a bunch of fucking maggots living underneath Ymir's dead skin! And these things, they're fucking nasty, you know, like the fucking upholstery on a public bus nasty. But then in one of his rare fucking displays of affection towards another living creature, Odin actually decides not to murder them or torture them into running circles in outer space till the end of fucking time, but instead he gives them some human intelligence and transforms them all into a bunch of little fucking dwarves. And one of them, his name is Gandalf, and the others, they all got names like Dvalin and Bombor and shit.[15]

Now all this shit, everything, Asgard, Middle-Earth, the holes in the ground that Gandalf and his buddies live in, everything, it's all part of the big ass world tree gallows pole contraption that exists in outer fucking space. And the tree itself, it's got these three huge roots, right? So, like, the first one, it goes down into Niflheim, you know, the land of ice, and down there, there's this mean fucking serpent that nibbles on it.[16] As for the other two roots, one of them

---

15   As discussed in this volume's Introduction, Tolkien borrowed extensively from Norse mythology, including the literal names of the dwarves, one of whom he made into a very Odinesque wizard figure. The behaviorisms, physical characteristics, and habitats of Tolkien's dwarves were also directly based on those found in the Norse myths.

16   This "mean fucking serpent" is the long-duration gamma-ray burst known as Níðhöggr the Dragon as identified in the "Old

goes into Asgard and Vanaheim—where all the sex gods[17] live—and Elf World, which is where all the people who look like Cate Blanchett and Orlando Bloom live, but they're all mysterious and shit and don't get out much. And then the last root goes into Middle-Earth and Giant Land, where all the dipshits live. And connecting Asgard to Middle-Earth is Bifrost, the rainbow bridge, which back then had a lot less implications about sexuality than it does nowadays.[18]

So the root that goes up into the land of the gods also goes to where the norns live, and these norns, they just sit around all day weaving like a fucking factory floor of spinning machines from the fucking height of the Industrial Revolution, only they're weaving the fucking lives of people instead of military uniforms or whatever. And it's weird too, some of these norns are nice girls, you know, but some of them are some real fucking bitches, and so whether you end up being a good person with a good life or a bad person with a bad life is all just dumb luck depending on which norn wove your fate. So guy like Bobby Orr, he had a wicked good norn weaving the story of his life, but guy like Aaron Hernandez, he got his life woven by a real fucking nasty norn during his conception, which is why he turned out to be such a fucking loser.[19]

Norse Astrophysics" section of introductory material.

[17]   The "sex gods" who live in Vanaheim are otherwise known as the Vanir while the more war-mongering gods such as Odin and Thor who live in Asgard are known as the Aesir. See "Old Norse Racial Diversity" in the introductory material for more about the two different tribes of gods, as well as the other various inhabitants of the 9 Worlds of Norse mythology.

[18]   Compared to Snorri Sturluson, the author of *The Prose Edda*, the poet of *The Impudent Edda* glosses over the 9 Worlds purported to support life within the Old Norse universe with very little detail or description. A complete listing and description of the 9 Worlds is provided in "A Brief Overview of the 9 Worlds" found in this book's introductory material.

[19]   Aaron Hernandez was the former New England Patriot tight end who murdered a semi-professional football player named, quite ironically, Odin Llyod, in North Attleborough, Massachusetts in

How Not to Get Away
with Witch Murder

All right, so now the world's brand spanking new, and Odin decides to celebrate his holy creation by going and murdering a fucking witch.[20]

Now I'm not real sure why he chose to celebrate in this particular manner, but I guess he just got real in touch with his inner Spanish Inquisitor one day or something because he just flipped the fuck out and nailed her ass with his fucking spear—and no, I don't mean his dick, although he does wave that thing around a lot, too.[21]

2013. Further adding to the irony, Hernandez was later found dead in his jail cell on April 19, 2017, having hung himself in symbolic Odinic fashion (see the myth titled *Odin Commits Suicide* for relevant Norse details).

[20] This witch has been identified as Gullveig from the poem, *Völuspá*, in *The Poetic Edda*. She is neither mentioned nor identified in *The Prose Edda*.

[21] It should be noted that there is ambiguity surrounding this event in the *Völuspá*'s rendition. This ambiguity leaves open the possibility that the witch was actually none other than Freyja herself, having come to visit and pay her respects to Odin and his brethren from her home in Vanaheim. The ambiguity further implies the possibility that Freyja was actually gang raped by the Aesir, thereby giving the Vanir a much stronger reason to go to war than their supposed third-party concern about the well-being of a random, wandering witch. The poet of *The Impudent Edda* follows the more common tradition related to the event in which the Vanir are portrayed as simply looking for an excuse to pick a fight with the Aesir.

Because the archaeological record has thus far produced no material evidence pertaining to the religious beliefs as specifically espoused in The Impudent Edda, *we must rely on the existing artifacts that have been found (primarily in Scandinavia and other parts of Northern Europe) to gain a better understanding of how the Bostonians might have viewed, depicted, and worshipped Odin, Thor, and the other Norse deities in the early 2000s. Here, we see a bronze figurine of Odin found in Lindby, Sweden. Ornately detailed, it quite clearly depicts Odin as a slavering fiend hell-bent on witch-murder; the media at the time were absolutely ruthless.*

So anyway, he impaled this witch with his fucking spear. But being a witch and all, she kept coming back to life, and so in order to successfully murder her, he had to keep on stabbing her over and over and over again till, eventually, he had to just fucking set her whole fucking body on fire just to keep her down.

Well, this was a wicked bad display of hospitality on his part, and it actually kind of reflected poorly on all the other gods, too, since witches were usually pretty well liked back in those days, even if this one was a total fucking criminal. And honestly, I don't really know why Odin went all psycho-killer on her ass, but soon as word got out about it, he had a major fucking PR debacle to deal with, and you know how he is—sometimes he's poetic as fuck, but other times you'd think he's a bonafide fucking

shit-head completely in-fucking-capable of formulating coherent
sentences on his own accord on account of all the crap that comes
spewing out of his mouth. And so, of course, the media just eats
this up like fucking flies on dog shit, and so next thing you know,
the Vanir are watching this guy declare on live fucking television
that the slaughter was justified since the witch was a real nasty
woman, corrupt to the fucking core, and who no one even liked
anyway except for other evil women, and he'd fucking kill them
all too if he could.

I don't know, the whole thing kind of reminds me of American
politics, maybe only a little bit classier.

But anyway, talk about stabbing yourself in the fucking foot
because now those Vanir guys decide this gives them the perfect
excuse to launch a full scale attack on Asgard just like they've always been wanting to do all along. So now war breaks out and it's
a fucking shit show because it just drags on and on and on and on
for fucking like forever, and pretty soon both Asgard and Vanaheim end up getting leveled to the fucking ground. And so now
they're both looking like Berlin's long lost twins from 1945, and,
of course, the gods grew up pretty priviledged and don't really like
sleeping on empty streets full of rubble and ashes and ruins, and
so they figure, you know, maybe it's about time to hold a cease
fire so they can at least try to patch up their differences and get
back to the stuff that's actually important to them like getting
wasted and having lots of casual sex with giants and dwarves and
horses and shit.

So the gods hold this peace summit, and the way this works is
they all spit into this huge-ass vat as a symbol of their good intentions, and then they take this giant wad of spit and shape it into
the form of a man, and then they send this goofy-assed bastard[22]

---

[22]   Known as Kvasir, this "goofy-assed" spit-mutant's role in *The
Impudent Edda* is an unconventional blending of those found in
the *Skáldskaparmál* section of *The Prose Edda* and the *Ynglinga
Saga* section of the *Heimskringla*. It is interesting to note that

off into Middle-Earth to try and educate all the people living over there for good samaritan type reasons since he's so wise on account of being made out of a bunch of the gods' fucking saliva and all.

But the two sides also decide to exchange some captives with each other, and so Njord, Frey, and Freyja from the Vanir side all go off to live at Asgard while Hoenir and Mimir from the Aesir side go off to live at Vanaheim. And this works out all right for a while, I guess, but eventually the Vanir start feeling like they got shafted on the deal because they realize that Hoenir's basically as dumb as a fucking brick. So one day when he wasn't around, they cornered Mimir and chopped his fucking head off, and then they sent it back to Odin out of retaliation.[23]

---

the *Skáldskaparmál* and *Ynglinga Saga* differ since they were both written by the same guy. Clearly, sometimes Snorri got lazy, or at the very least distracted by one of his many plots to overthrow medieval Iceland's system of democratic rule.

[23] *The Impudent Edda*'s details on the exchange of hostages and subsequent murder and decapitation of Mimir are not corroborated in either *The Poetic* or *Prose Eddas*, although the general proceedings are closely aligned with those found in *Ynglinga Saga*.

Odin Sends Freyja a Dick Pic*

Now the thing is, Odin just absolutely loves decapitated talking heads. That's why he was so fucking overwhelmed with joy and elation when Mimir's decapitated fucking head showed up on his front doorstep. Because at first Odin was kind of like, "Goddamnit, those fucking hippie assholes out on the West Coast killed my buddy!" when he opened up the box and he saw Mimir's dead head staring straight back at him from beneath the styrafoam peanuts, but then when he realized that he got a new decapitated head to add to his collection and that this one talked on top of it all, he was like, "Holy shit, I hit the fucking jackpot!" The one downside was that this new disembodied version of Mimir refused to tell him all the wise shit he'd learned about making award-winning wine or the defensive weaknesses of the Giants' stadium unless Odin poked his own eye out, but being as Odin was already planning on committing suicide pretty soon anyway, he figured he could handle this.[24]

---

[24] Both *The Poetic Edda*'s *Völuspá* and *The Prose Edda*'s *Gylfaginning* elaborate on the rather curt description provided by *The Impudent Edda* regarding the sacrifice that Odin makes of his own eye to Mimir's levitating, decapitated head. According to these older sources, Mimir's head guards a special well of interplanetary cosmic radiation that is located less than a single parsec away

---

* *This myth is the first of nine found in* The Impudent Edda *that is not attested to in either of the Elder Eddas or other medieval source material.*

Now everyone always thinks that Odin and Mimir only ever talk about thoughtful, philosophical type shit having to do with the meaning of life as a divine entity or the Red Sox's own spotty history of questionable management decisions or whatever, but the truth of the matter is, they're both a couple of fucking perverts, and so most of the time when Odin's hanging out with Mimir, their minds are diving down deeper into the gutter than a fucking high school hockey team's. I mean, when you get a creepy old man and an even creepier talking head together, just what the fuck do you think they're going to talk about?

So it's only a matter of time before one day Mimir, in all his wise fucking wisdom, comes up with the brilliant idea to send Freyja a fucking dick pic. And, of course, Odin's like, "Dude, you're a fucking genius!" Because you know, he totally thinks he's getting his gouged-eye-out's worth out of Mimir for thinking up shit like this.

But, of course, this didn't occur without some contentious difficulties, though, since Mimir never got over the fact that he'd been decapitated while visiting California,[25] and so now he has no fucking body. And being that it was his bright idea to send Freyja a dick pic in the first place, he thinks he should get to be the one

---

from the asymptotic giant branch of the space-time continuum nearest to Giant Land. The free neutrons found inside this well are inherently unstable, resulting in radioactive beta decay, the emitted neutrinos of which are absorbed by Mimir's skull and stochastically restabilized into a source of arcane knowledge. When Odin approached Mimir's head with a desire to absorb the cosmic well's neutrinos and gain their knowledge for himself, Mimir first demanded that he poke his own eye out as payment. Odin gladly obliged and became much smarter, hence his nickname, All-Knowing.

25   The anonymous poet of *The Impudent Edda* provides an important new detail here for scholars of Eddic studies. The implication that Vanaheim, the home of the Vanir, might be located in California is highly revelatory and requires further investigation.

to do it, but he can't since his body's in the process of decompos-
ing and being devoured by fish as it floats out past fucking Sau-
salito at this point, and so for him it's a real fucking lost cause.

Mimir just doesn't have a fucking dong anymore.

But Odin does, and so they bicker for a while, and then Mimir
finally fucking concedes because what's he going to do anyway?
He's only a magical talking fucking head; he's got no arms to use
to take the photo with even if he did still have a wiener. And so
Odin lifts up his fucking Gandalf robe, and he snaps a shot of his
one-eyed warrior, and then he texts it to Freyja who at this point
already thinks Odin is a total prick[26] but she isn't expecting to see
his literal prick pop up on her fucking phone, either.

So a few minutes go by and then Odin's phone starts blowing
up with angry texts from Freyja and every other goddamn goddess
from here to fucking Dwarf World. I mean, everyone's fucking
turning against Odin now including his own frigging wife, Frigg,
who's chewing his ass out and telling him to just stay in Mimir's
shitty cave and not even bother to come home. Everyone except
Loki, that is. Loki just sends Odin a text that says, "Nice one,
bro!" with one of those dumb, little cartoon winky face things.[27]

---

26   While not explicitly stating it, the anonymous poet may
potentially be alluding to Odin's prior act of unprovoked witch
murder and the possibility that the murdered witch, Gullveig,
may have been Freyja herself (as previously mentioned in footnote 21). While the textual evidence for Gullveig's actual identity
remains inconclusive, many documented instances exist in which
Odin and Loki have conspired to potentially sell or trade Freyja to
the giants. These instances all occur later in the mythological story arc, but the Eddic space-time continuum has always followed
a very fluid, rather than rigid, linear trajectory. Exacerbating this
fact in the case of *The Impudent Edda* is the otherwise unsubstantiated prevalence of smartphones reported to exist in ancient
Asgard. Regardless of any discrepancies in or contradictions to
the Eddic conception of time and space, it is only reasonable that
Freyja is not a huge fan of Odin.

27   Given his future history of poor decision-making, it is un-

The scene of Mimir's murder; a silent (and presumably divine) witness stands guard as Mimir's headless body sinks beneath the waves.

And well, what do you think Odin does when his phone finally stops buzzing?

He sends Freyja another dick pic.

I mean, it's like he somehow got more addicted to sending Freyja dick pics than to drinking mead with blood in it or listening to ravens whisper secret knowledge into his gnarly old ears. Like, he just can't stop doing it now, and Mimir's not helping matters any since he's projecting his own bullshit Napoleon Complex vicariously through Odin at this point. And so, eventually,

---

surprising that Loki would condone Odin's actions. Additionally, he and Odin are identified as blood brothers in *The Poetic Edda*'s poem, *Lokasenna*, so when the anonymous poet credits Loki with dialogue referring to Odin as "bro," the word operates both literally and figuratively.

Freyja has to change numbers, and this is why she hardly ever leaves Folkvangr anymore. Well, that, and the fact that Odin also has a real bad habit of letting Loki convince him to try and barter her off to the giants as part of whatever shitty deal the two of them happen to be cooking up at any given time.

I don't know. For supposedly being so fucking wise and shit, sometimes the gods and their magic talking heads are just a bunch of dumb fucking idiots.

Wicked Good Dwarf Treasure

All right, so this one night Thor was out massacring the giants over in Giant Land, since that's what he likes to do after having too many pints at the bar, and his wife Sif got lonely and pissed that he'd chosen to go drinking and giant-slaying again instead of spending some quality time with her, and so she decided to go and fuck Loki. Now Loki's loyal to no one, and so he goes for it since Sif's pretty fucking hot. So they have their one-night stand, and then when Loki wakes up in the morning, he sees Sif is still asleep, and so he goes and shaves off all her fucking hair from her head! He thought it was wicked funny, but Sif was pissed when she woke up and he was nowhere in sight and all her fucking hair was gone.[28]

And so then when Thor gets home later that day he's like, "What the fuck happened to your fucking hair?!" And, naturally, Sif can't tell him the truth, and so she lies and says she'd been asleep when Loki snuck into the house and cut it all off since he's a degenerate who likes to fuck with people. And Thor pretty much buys this hook, line, and sinker since he's a pretty trusting guy and not exactly the brightest bulb on the block, either, and

---

28 The *Skáldskaparmál* in *The Prose Edda* specifically states that Loki's shearing of Sif's golden hair was just a prank, without any implication of sexual relations between the two. However, in the *Lokasenna* from *The Poetic Edda*, Loki declares that he had an affair with Sif, though it remains unclear and uncertain whether he was lying and, if not, whether that affair occurred during the same time period as when he shaved her head. *The Impudent Edda*'s stance is clearly that this was, in fact, the case.

so once he hears that Loki's to blame, he marches straight on over to his house and threatens to murder the crazy bastard right then and there on his fucking doorstep if he doesn't do something to rectify the situation immediately.

And, you know, Loki, even though he's kind of a sick fuck, he likes being alive, and, honestly, he can't believe his good luck that Thor's too dumb to realize what really happened. And so he just agrees, and he goes and he gets in his beat-up old Buick, and he drives off over the rainbow bridge on his way to visit the dwarves at their clubhouse over in fucking Dwarf World. Now Dwarf World's a real shithole with lots of car-jackings happening all over the place, but Loki's not too worried about it because who'd want to steal that piece of shit that he drives, especially when most of the guys who live out there ride Harleys? So anyway, he parks it out front, and then he tries to crawl into the clubhouse through the tiny little entrance that looks like its made for fucking pee-wees since we are talking about dwarves here after all and all.

So, of course, he gets his head stuck in the door jamb since it's too fucking small, and now he can hardly even move, and so he's just stuck there squirming like a fucking moron when the Sons of Ivaldi, who'd all just been sitting around, playing pool, counting their cash, and discussing their ongoing criminal affairs, suddenly go real quiet because now they got this intruder blocking their entrance with his huge fucking head and stealing all the oxygen in the room. And the thing is, the Sons of Ivaldi aren't the types of guys you want to fuck with. I mean, these guys, they might be wicked diminutive, but they are some real hardcore mother-fuckers, you know? Like, I'm talking about black leather, tattoos, shaved heads, and some serious fucking beards that hang all the way down to the ground, even if that is only like a couple of feet or so.[29]

---

29   It is not clear how or why the dwarves evolved from the traditional depictions found in the Elder Eddas (and most modern fantasy novels) into a group of dimunitive bikers distributed among an

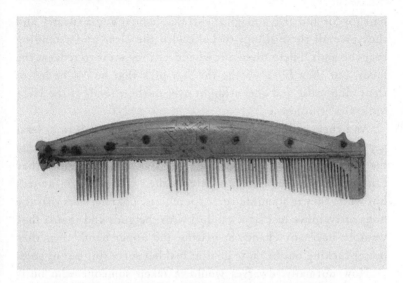

*It has been suggested that Sif used a comb made of bone,
similar to this one found in Björkö, Sweden, to comb
her long, luscious, golden hair, both before and after her
notorious head-shearing incident.*

But anyway, so the Sons of Ivaldi are like, "Hey, who the
fuck are you and what the fuck are you doing here?" And so
Loki launches into what he considers to be a real steller business
proposition, which is basically for them to help him out with
the manufacture of some golden goods in exchange for winning
the favor of the gods. And so the Sons of Ivaldi, they actually
think this is a sweet idea since winning the favor of the gods'll
give them a leg up on their rivals over in the Hel's Valkyries
club. So these guys fire up their forges, and they get to work and
before you even know it, they've made some special replacement

---

indeterminate number of rival gangs in *The Impudent Edda*. One
possible influence for this evolution could be the impact of the
Great Nordic Biker War that raged throughout Scandinavia in the
late 1990s, during the course of which twelve people were killed
and ninety-six were wounded.

hair for Sif and also a magical shrinkable boat and a spear,[30] and
they give all these things to Loki with the clear understanding
that the gods'll help them out whenever they want to redeem the
favor, but then Loki—being the shit-pick that he is—he leaves
their clubhouse and goes straight over to their rivals at the Hel's
Valkryies' clubhouse!

And their clubhouse is a bit bigger, so he manages to at least
get his whole head in through the door before getting stuck at
his shoulders, and now everyone's just staring at him since they
can't believe this jack-off just entered their clubhouse uninvited,
but while they're standing there speechless, Loki declares that the
Sons of Ivaldi've just struck a deal with the gods and that if they
want to have any chance at getting the upper hand, then they
better fucking outdo those guys at making some shit out of gold.

Now normally, dwarves would've taken someone who busts
into their place like that out back and put a fucking bullet in their
head, but since Loki was talking about winning the favor of the
gods over their rivals, they thought, "Hey, you know, maybe it's
in our best interests to listen to him," and so they started revving
up their forges to fucking like 7500 rpms, and then blasted off
soon as the light turned green and made a gold pig, a gold ring,
and a gold hammer.[31]

---

[30]   These magical artifacts have been identifed in the Elder Eddas as Skíðblaðnir, Frey's special boat that possesses the ability to
be folded up like a handkerchief so that he can put it in his pocket
when he doesn't want to sail it, and Gungnir, Odin's spear.

[31]   As with the magical artifacts created by the Sons of Ivaldi, the
poet of *The Impudent Edda* does not divulge much detail about
those created by the Hel's Valkyries, either. The first, Gullinbursti,
is known from the Elder Eddas to be the golden boar that pulls
Frey's chariot. The second is Odin's ring, Draupnir, that drips
eight new rings from itself every ninth night. Draupnir is cultur-
ally important to the 20th and 21st centuries because it, along
with the famous ring from *Völsunga Saga*, helped directly inspire
the more popular legend of the one ring to rule them all, to find

So now these Hel's Valkyries guys, they're not as trusting as the Sons of Ivaldi, and they know that Loki's a double-crossing piece of shit, so they insist on keeping an eye on him all the way back to Asgard, and Loki knows he can't say no or they'll cap his ass. So off they all go, and when they all get there Loki makes this big presentation to the gods about the gold shit made by the Sons of Ivaldi and the Hel's Valkyries, and then he asks them to say which is best so as to give them their favor.

And that did not go exactly as he had hoped for because, well for starters, neither Odin nor Thor were happy that he brought this fucking gang into Asgard. These guys are members of the criminal dwarf underworld, and Odin doesn't want any sort of drug trafficking to start making its way through his home. I mean, he doesn't want any trouble with the fucking cartels, you know? And he doesn't really give a shit about who's better at goldsmithery, either, and so he declares real fucking fast that the Hel's Valkyries guys are the best since they're the ones who're there in Asgard at that particular moment, and then he turns into a fucking raven[32] and flies away to try and find some dead bodies to nibble on.

And so the Hel's Valkyries guys go home feeling like a million bucks about having gained the favor of the gods over the Sons of

---

them all, to bring them all, and to (in the darkness) bind them all. Finally, the third magical artifact is Mjölnir, Thor's hammer.

[32] Odin's transformation into a raven is the first instance in *The Impudent Edda* that illustrates his ability to break the symmetry of his own constituent god particles through various states of quantum excitation as a means to alter his mass and assume a different form. He has always been an enigmatic figure, and when he poked his own eye out as described in the myth, *Odin Sends Freyja a Dick Pic*, his fundamental god particles underwent a unique generation mechanism that yielded this new ability to either reduce or increase his mass at will (or become entirely massless), which he henceforth took full advantage of whenever he wished to shape-shift into another humanoid or animal form.

*The sort of shady Svartelfheim establishment that Loki
enjoys dropping in on completely uninvited.*

Ivaldi, and then as soon as they're gone, Thor clocks Loki right
in the fucking face and then he goes and gives the golden wig to
his wife.[33]

---

[33]   In general, *The Impudent Edda*'s version of this myth deviates
substantially from the earlier extant version found in *The Prose
Edda*'s *Skáldskaparmál* in terms of both the identification and the
specific role of the second gang of dwarves. *The Prose Edda* identifies these dwarves as the two brothers, Brokk and Eitri, rather
than as an entire club of Hel's Valkyries. Additionally, during
the forging process, Loki repeatedly transforms himself into a
fly to harass Brokk while he works the bellows, which results in
a mistakenly shortened handle for Thor's hammer. Brokk then
travels back to Asgard with Loki because he and Eitri do not to
trust the trickster. In the course of winning the favor of the gods,
Brokk also earns the privilege of literally sewing Loki's mouth
shut, which he does with great glee while all the other gods watch

Odin Commits Suicide

So one day Odin gets to thinking it'd be a wicked good idea to commit suicide, so he goes and he fucking impales himself with his own fucking spear.[34]

And then as if that wasn't hardcore enough, he goes and he hangs himself with a noose from Yggdrasil,[35] and so now his dead body's just dangling there, his neck stretched longer than a fucking python, and he's got a goddamned spear sticking out of his abdomen.

But then after like nine days, he comes back to life, and now he knows how to carve the runes, so I guess it was worth it.[36]

---

and laugh.

[34] This spear is commonly acknowledged to be Gungnir, which Odin received from the Hel's Valkyries dwarf biker gang as related in the previous myth, *Wicked Good Dwarf Treasure*, as part of the highly suspicious black market arms deal brokered by the always nebulous trickster god, Loki.

[35] As discussed in footnote 1 in the myth, *Cosmological Frost Giant Genocide*, Yggdrasil means "Gallows Pole" in Old Norse, and another one of its nicknames is "Odin's Steed," a properly fatalistic reference to Odin riding the gallows, as he does here.

[36] To the Norsemen and women of yore, the runes were not simply just alphabetic characters as they are commonly misconceived to be today. The runes held great power, and the carving of them was an act akin to casting magical spells in modern fantasy stories. The *Hávamál* of *The Poetic Edda*, in particular, discusses at great length the importance of the runes, making it self-explanatory as to why a grim, virulent god such as Odin would be so

One quality that the ancient Scandinavians and modern Bostonians undisputedly share is the willingness to fully submit to the magical properties of words displayed on tablets, whether they be carved into immovable stone or electronically displayed on easily transportable devices. This example of the former is from Scania, Sweden and clearly illustrates the runic script that Odin killed himself to learn. It reads: "Tonne raised this stone for her spouse Bram together with his son Asgot. He was the best of land owners and gave generously away his food." These, clearly, are important qualities during any time period.

willing to sacrifice himself to himself to gain their powers. Among the runes praised in the *Hávamál* are those that grant their carver the ability to resurrect and have meaningful conversations with corpses found hanging in trees, the ability to get out of jail free (fake American currency did not exist in medieval Scandinavia, so the alternate to getting out of jail free was usually dying rather than paying an arbitrary $50 funny money fee), and the ability to seduce any attractive young woman without resorting to physical force (a rare thing among plunderers in the viking glory days), no matter how reluctant she might be.

Thor Begets the Green Monster*

So one day Thor decides it'd be wicked pisser[37] to go and kill some fucking trolls, and so he goes and he gets his goats[38] out, and he takes them for a spin over in Iron Wood[39] where all the nasty troll women live. So he's out there now, riding along and getting deeper and deeper into the deep, dark woods, and it's starting to get all marshy and untamed since Olmsted's not

---

[37] Properly pronounced as "wicked pissah," this is a New England colloquialism basically equating to "super cool." It has been maintained in this translation for its authentic tone. "Wicked" alone basically means "very."

[38] Thor's primary mode of transportation is, and has always been, a dual goat-powered cart of war.

[39] Iron Wood, also known as Járnviðr, is the home of monstrous troll women and supernatural demon wolves. The Elder Eddas attest that Mânegarm, the wolf who will swallow the moon during the final cataclysmic, supernovaic universe-shattering event, was born in Iron Wood. *The Prose Edda* goes further than *The Poetic Edda* in its details, and declares that Mânegarm will also feast on the souls of doomed men and spatter the sky with their blood and gore, obscuring the photons emitted by our sun as they enter the near-space atmosphere, bringing darkness and despair to every continent on the planet.

* *This myth is the second of nine found in* The Impudent Edda *that is not attested to in either of the Elder Eddas or other medieval source material.*

done his landscaping yet,[40] and it's all stagnant and smelly and shit, when he finally starts coming across all these stupid little troll houses.

So he parks his goats and he feeds the meter, and then he knocks on the door of the first house he sees and as soon as the nasty ass troll who lives there opens up, Thor just fucking smashes her brains in with his fucking hammer!

Now you might be wondering what the fuck kind of asshole murders some horrid bitch like that without any sort of provocation, but the fact of the matter is, she had some innocent little kids boiling in a stew in her cauldron back in the kitchen that she was planning on eating later so, you know, she had it coming. These are evil fucking trolls we're talking about here, not normal, everyday decent folk.

So Thor continues on his rampage, going door to door, house to house, and the body count's really starting to pile up when he finally has to take a piss, so he stops off at the duck house by the bridge[41] to relieve his poor, aching bladder. So now he's just standing there, letting it all flow freely when all of a sudden he hears something growl, and so he turns and looks over his shoulder, and he sees this gigantic goddamned demon wolf staring him straight in the fucking face. And this wolf looks mean. I mean, its fangs are bared, and it's looking like it's about ready to fucking pounce and rip poor Thor to shreds. And poor Thor, man! He's

---

[40] In another example of the non-linear fluidity of the Norse conceptualization of the space-time continuum, the anonymous poet here seems to have antedated the existence of certain features of Boston's Back Bay Fens prior to the actual development of the area into a parkland (for which the antedated features were built). The project in question was designed by Frederick Law Olmsted, a preeminent American landscape architect who is best known for designing New York City's Central Park.

[41] The bridge under discussion crosses Boston's Muddy River. Beside this bridge lies the Agassiz Road Duck House, a cute but now dilapidated 19th century restroom facility.

The Agassiz Road Duck House in the Boston Back Bay Fens where Thor once relieved his aching bladder and was almost mauled by a monstrous wolf in the process.

only mid-stream, you know, so of course, he's still got his hands down on his package, and so he's completely in-fucking-capacitated. And he'd set his hammer down on the paper towel dispenser when he walked in anyway, and so, you know, he's looking at this wolf going, "Shit, I'm fucked!"

But just then this gorgeous fucking girl bursts into the restroom and chops the wolf's fucking head off with a sword since she's a fucking shield maiden. Now this is kind of awkward for Thor since he's still incapacitated by his super long stream of thunder-piss, but pretty soon he finishes up, and then he thanks her for saving his sorry ass, and she invites him back to her place over in Sökkvabekkr[42] where they then proceed to get drunk,

---

42 Sökkvabekkr has been identified as a possible alternate name for Fensalir, the marshy, fen-based home of Frigg (Odin's wife), and Sága as an alternate name for Frigg herself. While the truth of this matter remains unclear, it is nonetheless atypical for Sága to spend

Wally the Green, youngest son of Thor, is said to slumber somewhere in this lair till the coming of Ragnarök, whence he will awaken and join the forces of good versus evil (and New York) in the battle to end all battles.

which is one of Thor's most favorite things to do—right up there with killing trolls and giants.

So now these two are knocking back the beers, and Thor's starting to get real philosophical on his various points of view about proper beard hygiene and maintenance since he's got a real nice fluffy red one, but this is boring the living daylights out of poor fucking Sága who just eventually tells him to shut the fuck up and drags him back to her bedroom where she proceeds to ride him like a wild fucking animal.

---

her time cavorting with Thor as occurs in *The Impudent Edda*. The *Grímnismál* from *The Poetic Edda* in particular states that Odin is her preferred booze/sex mate. *The Impudent Edda* is also the only source to imply that Sága is a part-troll shield-maiden.

So then when Thor wakes up the next morning, he has a huge fucking hangover and can't remember for his life where the fuck he parked his goats, and so off he goes to look for them, and nine months later Sága gives birth to this woolly green monster who's actually a pretty nice guy despite being a genetic calamity, but he's also dumb as a fucking brick and part troll, and so when he walks out into the sunlight like his mom's told him not to do a thousand times already, he just turns into fucking stone right then and there. And so now he's stuck there, frozen solid like a goddamned wall in the middle of the fens for everyone to see and getting baseballs hit at him[43] till the end of fucking time when everyone and everything will die in a huge fucking fire.

---

43 *The Impudent Edda* is the only authentic source of Scandinavian mythology to suggest that the legendary leftfield wall at Boston's Fenway Park is actually descended from a mostly noble but somewhat blemished lineage of gods, shield-maidens, and trolls.

Loki Gets Boned by a Horse

So one day this fucking blacksmith shows up in Asgard, and he says to the gods, "Hey, so how about if I build you the best fucking fortress you've ever fucking seen?" And if that isn't suspect then I don't now what is. I mean, an offer like that's like finding a fucking begger sitting on a street corner giving out free money. It just doesn't fucking make sense.

And so, naturally, the gods are like, "What the fuck?" Because they weren't born fucking yesterday, and so they ask him what he wants in return, and he's like, "Let me marry Freyja. And also, I want to own the sun and the moon as my own personal property."

Now the gods, being the devious bunch of bastards that they are, they get to thinking that maybe they can outsmart this guy, you know, and create a win-win sort of situation for themselves. So in the end they tell him, "All right, it's a deal, but only if you can finish building the fortress before the winter's over."

And I'm sure Freyja was just totally psyched about this one because you know how it is, sometimes winter doesn't fucking end till like April or even May some years, and so they got a real indeterminate deadline they're working with here, and so of course, this sort of lack of loyalty from the home team only just reinforces her tendency to be a fucking cat lady who stays at home and roots for the fucking Habs.[44]

---

[44] Just as Thor has his goats to help him get around, Freyja keeps cats for her preferred mode of transportation; her chariot is pulled by two such felines. It is unknown exactly how many cats

So anyway, though, they all strike this deal, and the blacksmith asks them if he can use his horse,[45] and Loki, being the cocky prick that he is, answers and he's like, "Yeah, you know, why not? Give the guy a break, you know, it's just one fucking horse is all." And then the smith and the gods all take a bunch of oaths not to betray each other which is a fucking joke since they're all just basically a pack of wild dogs that can't be trusted—with the exception of Thor who wasn't even there to take the oath on account of the fact that he was out of town, creating thunderstorms, and hammering on some fucking trolls out in Iron Wood again.

But that horse of the smith's, turns out he's a real fucking worker, and he's good, too. I mean, the animal makes Bobby Orr look like a fucking quadriplegic on skates. Seriously, at the rate this horse is going, it's got the gods starting to shit their pants since they only got three days of winter left. And Freyja's really starting to freak the fuck out, and so now she's taking in every fucking stray she finds out on the streets into her house to try and console herself with and get her mind off the matter.

Now at this point, the gods all turn on Loki because he's the guy who told the blacksmith, "Oh yeah, man, go ahead and use

---

she owns because none of the other gods have ever dared broach the subject, but rumors have always suggested that the number is very high. She also likes pigs and keeps the battle swine, Hildisvíni, as one of her other household pets at her hall, Sessrúmnir, where he is allowed to frolick and forage among the wild flowers of the meadow, Fólkvangr, right outside its doors. According to the *Hyndluljóð* (an ancient Norse poem found in the *Flateyjarbók* but frequently included in English-language translations of *The Poetic Edda*), Hildisvíni is a golden pig and the gift of dwarves, much like Gullinbursti was for Freyja's brother, Frey, as described in the myth, *Wicked Good Dwarf Treasure*. Finally, "Habs" is a nickname for the Montreal Canadiens, the archrivals of the Boston Bruins (Odin's favorite team) in the National Hockey League.
[45] This horse has been identified as Svaðilfari in *The Prose Edda*'s *Gylfaginning* as well as the *Hyndluljóð*.

your fucking horse, that's no big deal." And so they threaten Loki that if he don't find a way out of this fucking mess then they're going to chop his fucking balls off.

So Loki, being the shape-shifting sleazeball that he is, he decides to go and transform himself into a fucking mare in heat,[46] and then he, uh…I guess, he just goes and he frolicks on over to by where that smith's horse is, or whatever it is horses do when they're feeling horny. And so that succeeds in distracting that other horse, and he chases Loki off into the bushes and basically rapes him. Or maybe it was consensual horse sex. I really don't know but, either way, Loki must have found it preferable to getting castrated or murdered by Ole One-Eye[47] and his thugs.

---

[46]   Here, Loki clearly demonstrates an ability to manipulate his field of quantum excitation to break his own symmetry as a means to alter both the amount of mass that comprises his fundamental state and the chemical properties that comprise his inert molecular structure. Odin's ability to do the same was briefly discussed in footnote 32 in the myth, *Wicked Good Dwarf Treasure*, but much to the dismay of modern scientists, no source of Norse mythology has ever attempted to explain why only a select retinue of gods and giants possess these fundamental god particle altering abilities; it is generally presumed that this is simply knowledge that has been lost to the mists of time. Despite their eternal antagonism, gods and giants are similar beings, and, under the ancient Norse scientific belief system, it stands to reason that there would be others besides Odin (such as Loki) who, through undisclosed acts of macabre self-mutilation, might also obtain the ability to similarly manipulate their own constituent god particles.

[47]   "Ole One-Eye" is one of Odin's many nicknames as well as a good example of a kenning, a word or phrase used to refer to a given subject in descriptive terms without relying on its actual title or name. In this case, Ole One-Eye is a reference to Odin poking his own eye out at the Well of Mimir as described in the myth, *Odin Sends Freyja a Dick Pic*. Kennings could be applied to any number of things and were common throughout the ancient Germanic world. One of the most well-known examples is "whale road," in reference to the sea, as occurs in the old English poem,

But at any rate, that fucked-up one night stand was enough to slow work down on the fortress to the point that the smith couldn't get it all done on time, and when this happens he goes into a huge fucking berserker rage, and now for the first time the gods all realize that this guy isn't just some ordinary smith from Middle-Earth but actually a goddamned frost giant. And how the hell they missed this at the beginning beats me. Sometimes the gods just got shit for brains.

So now they got this asshole who's wicked pissed on their hands, and the gods are all like, "Fuck!" So they send off for Thor to come back from his troll-hammering expedition, and when he shows up he's just like, "I AM FUCKING THOR!!!" And then he proceeds to just beat the living shit out of that fucking prick. And Freyja's just like, "Thank god," and all in all everyone's pretty fucking happy. And then like nine months later Loki gives birth to Sleipnir, the eight-legged wonder-horse who Odin rides around on till the end of time when a shitty wolf eats him alive.

Beowulf. Other kennings also occur in _The Impudent Edda_ but are not singled out with footnotes of their own.

Blood Spit Honey Death

So you remember that goofy bastard who the gods made out of their own spit?

Yeah, so that guy's name's Kvasir, and he's been going around all over Middle-Earth now trying to educate all the dumb asses about whatever's worth learning, but then he comes across some road construction, and the detour's marked so poorly that Paul Revere[48] couldn't have even found his way in broad fucking daylight, and so, of course, Kvasir's an out-of-towner, and so he doesn't even know where the fuck he's going in the first place. And so next thing you know, he's stuck on some fucking on-ramp headed straight into goddamned Dwarf World.

And the situation's completely fucking hopeless, you know? I mean, there's no way way he can turn back at this point, and so he's just like, "Eh, fuck it," since the dwarves could use an education, too, and he's offering his knowledge for a hell of a lot less than $60,000/year, so why not go and see if they're even the least bit interested, you know?

So he pulls up outside the first house he comes across, and he sees that the garage door is open, and he hears some noises coming out of it. So he gets out of his car, and he goes into the garage

---

48   An artful and poetic allusion to the midnight ride of Paul Revere, in which the famous silversmith rode from Boston westwards to Lexington and, eventually, Concord, to warn the colonial militia that the British were coming in 1775. The event preceded the "Shot Heard 'Round the World" and the start of the American Revolution.

Before he even realized what had happened, Kvasir was heading north on I-93 towards his ultimate demise at the hands of a couple of murderous biker dwarves.

where he sees a couple of dwarves[49] decked out in all the usual black leather and metal chains and shit, revving the engines of their fucking forges, talking about some sort of plot to extort the local town council so as to keep the police off their backs so that they can sell more hard liquor on the black market or whatever. So they look up as soon as they realize Kvasir's watching them, and they got no doubts he's already heard far too much, so before he even knows what's going on, the nastier of the two dwarves pulls out a pistol and shoots the poor bastard right in the fucking forehead.

---

[49] These dwarves have been identified as Fjalar and Galar in the *Skáldskaparmál* of *The Prose Edda*.

So now Kvasir's dead body's bleeding like a bitch since it's squishy soft on account of being made out of spit, and the dwarves are like, "Fuck! We need to get rid of this fucking thing before someone drives by and sees it!" And so they lug his corpse over to one of their forges, and they throw it into the fucking fire so as to dispose of it but there's still a gigantic puddle of blood and spit all over the floor of their garage, and so they mop it all up, and then they go and wring out the spit-blood into this huge ass vat that they got out back where they're brewing a special new batch of mead for their bootlegging enterprise. And since Kvasir was imbued with special magical knowledge, his spit-blood gives this mead some real special properties, too, in that, basically, everyone who drinks it gets wicked fucking poetic wicked fucking fast, which was a real big deal back then.

So now some time goes by and, eventually, this guy, Gilling who's a giant, comes into town with his wife to observe the world's oldest annual forge rally, and he figures, "Hey you know, why not pay a visit to these bootlegging dwarves? Maybe we can team up and expand their business into Giant Land since I've got good contacts there." And so the dwarves are like, "Yeah, okay, why not?" And so they suggest getting some beers and taking a boat out onto the lake for a while while they all talk it over. So the dwarves and Gilling get in the boat, and they leave his wife behind since she's a woman, and that's just how things were done back in those days. And so now they're slowly taking the boat through the channel, and they've barely gone past the old drive-in movie theater when those fucking dwarves intentionally crash the boat on some shallow rocks. And Gilling can't swim even though he's a giant in shallow water, and so he fucking drowns and dies, which the dwarves think is fucking hilarious.

So now they go back home and inform Gilling's wife that she's just become a widow due to some horrific nautical accident, and she's all sad and says she wants to see where it happened, and so they take her over to the beach and point out the site where the wreck happened. And while she's standing there crying, one of the dwarves climbs up onto the retaining wall that's supporting the street behind them and drops a fucking rock on her head, and then they go and tie some heavy rocks to her body and toss it into the lake to make it disappear.

Well, the cover up isn't exactly the most effective since there's a couple hundred thousand forge enthusiasts in town this week, and these dumb ass dwarves were in plain sight when they committed the crime. And so word of the murder spreads far and wide, and, eventually, makes its way back to Suttung who's Gilling's son, and he gets fucking pissed, and so a few days later he shows up outside the dwarves' house, breaks the fucking door down, and drags the two dwarves out of their beds and then proceeds to beat the living shit out of them. So now they black out due to the physical trauma, and then when they finally wake up again, they find themselves shackled to a fucking rock out somewhere in the middle of the North Atlantic at low tide with Suttung standing over them cackling like a fucking maniac because now the tide's starting to come in and he's going to get to watch those two fucking dwarves drown right before his very eyes.

So, of course, the dwarves freak the fuck out and start begging for their lives, and when they finally offer Suttung the special spit-blood poetry mead if he lets them go, he stops and thinks about it for a minute it, and then he's like, "Okay, that's cool."[50]

---

[50]   In general, *The Impudent Edda* closely follows *The Prose Edda*'s rendition of this myth, but fails to address the outcome of the deal struck between Suttung and the dwarves. According to Snorri, after releasing the dwarves and going home, Suttung gives the mead to his daughter, Gunnlöd, with strict instructions to safeguard it. Also missing from *The Impudent Edda* is any mention that the dwarves did, in fact, inform the gods that Kvasir had died, claiming that he had choked on his own knowledge, which the gods apparently believed because otherwise they would have surely sent Thor to destroy them with his mighty hammer.

Bad Poets Drink Bird Shit

So now Odin's getting jealous that this son of a bitch giant's got this special mead that makes whoever drinks it wicked good at poetry since Odin's the top dog god and also the god of poetry,[51] and he thinks he should have the mead, plus like Thor, he's a fucking alcoholic. So one day he decides he's going to go and steal the stuff, and so he gets on his eight-legged mustang, and he heads over the rainbow bridge going north on 93[52] since everyone knew where everyone else lived back in those days.

So he's cruising along now and he has just barely crossed the state border[53] when he decides to pull off to take a leak, and while he's at the rest stop he fucking murders these nine slaves,[54] who

---

[51] Bragi, Idunn's husband, is another significant god of poetry but he does not play a role in *The Impudent Edda*.

[52] While alluded to in the preceding myth in which Kvasir accidentally drives to Dwarf World, the particular reference here remains the only Eddic reference that directly correlates U.S. Interstate 93 and the Zakim Bridge in Boston with the otherwise ethereal Bifrost Bridge.

[53] Odin is now in New Hampshire. This unique detail about his quest for the mead is not corroborated by any other Eddic source.

[54] Here, the poet of *The Impudent Edda* presents Odin as more cold-blooded than he has been traditionally portrayed in other sources. According to *The Prose Edda*'s *Skáldskaparmál*, Odin disguises himself as a wanderer and takes the temporary name Bolverk, which is literally an Old Norse variant for "Evil-Doer." However, he does not overtly massacre the slaves as occurs in *The Impudent Edda*. Rather, the *Skáldskaparmál* relates that he discovers nine slaves

just so happened to be working there, before getting back on his horse and continuing on up into the mountains. Now, eventually, he gets to Baugi's B&B where he stays for the night, and when he gets up the next morning, Baugi starts bitching while he's making Odin his bacon and eggs about the fact that his nine slaves just got murdered the day before, and now he doesn't know how he's going to properly maintain his rest stop without actually having to pay someone to do the fucking work, to which Odin is like, "Hey, you know, if you let me stay here all summer long free of charge, I'll do the work of nine slaves provided you also help me get a swig of Suttung's special mead." Because Odin figured Baugi could help him out with this since Suttung's Baugi's brother.

Now Baugi's got no fucking idea that Odin is Odin, otherwise he never would have agreed to his offer. I mean, he just thinks Odin's some dumb fucking hobo who got tired of living in the city and that needs a job and won't in a million years be as effective as nine fucking slaves since that's not humanly possible. But Odin is Odin, and so he spends the next few months cleaning toilets and scrubbing floors, and he fucking wins the bet since he's a god and also a real master manipulator in these types of situations. And at this point Baugi realizes he'd better try and help Odin get a sip of Suttung's mead since he cares about keeping his word, which is weird since he's a fucking giant, which by default makes him an asshole, plus he used to own slaves, but whatever.

So anyway, these two guys head over together to the cabin at the base of the mountain where Suttung lives, and they inquire about the mead, and Suttung's like, "Ah, fuck no, I don't share that shit with anybody." And then he tells them both to go fuck

---

working in a field and offers to sharpen their scythes for them with a special whetstone. He then offers to sell the whetstone, and when all nine slaves start arguing amongst themselves about who gets to buy it, Odin tosses it up into the air, and in the commotion that ensues, the slaves all accidentally slit each other's throats with their scythes.

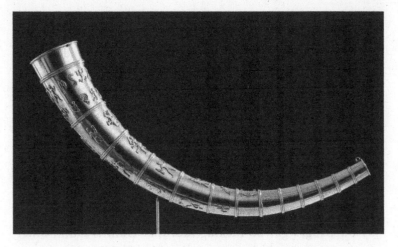

It is believed that Odin drank the Mead of Poetry from a glorious horn like this one from Gallehus, Denmark while he was holed up in a cave partaking in illicit relations with the daughter of an evil giant.

themselves, but Odin won't give up so easily, and so he coerces Baugi into drilling a hole straight into the heart of the fucking mountain since Odin obviously knows that the mead is hidden in the center of the mountain where it's being guarded by Gunnlöd, who is Suttung's daughter. And Baugi goes along with this for who knows why, and after he's done drilling the hole, Odin transforms himself into a fucking snake[55] and starts slithering through the hole, which is when Baugi finally realizes that Odin is Odin, and then he feels like a fucking moron.[56]

---

[55] Odin's transformation into a snake and subsequent transformation into an eagle in this myth are good examples of his ability to spontaneously break symmetry in order to alter the state of mass that comprises the molecular structure of his fundamental god particles.
[56] At this point in *The Prose Edda*'s version of this myth, Baugi attempts to kill Odin by whacking him with the tool that he used to drill through the mountain but fails since Odin is both all-knowing and all-wily.

And Odin makes his way through to the center of the mountain pretty quick, and when he pops his head out of the hole he's been slithering through, his jaw just fucking drops because Gunnlöd is fucking gorgeous. And she's fucking lonely. At first she's like, "Eh, it's just some dumb snake, maybe I can eat it since I'm getting sick and tired of oatmeal." But then when Odin transforms into his normal self, she gets hornier than a cat in heat. Odin might be a wrinkly old fuck, but he knows how to woo the ladies, especially when the ladies are trapped inside a mountain and never have any contact with anyone ever.

So the old geezer bangs Gunnlöd for fucking like three days straight, and all the while he's drinking all the mead that she's been tasked to guard, but she doesn't give a shit since she hates her dad anyway. And then when Odin's finally drinken it all, he decides to turn himself into an eagle and fly away since all he came for was the mead, and he doesn't really care about poor Gunnlöd.[57]

So he gets out of the mountain by magic, and then when Suttung sees him flying away, he realizes what's up, and so he also turns himself into an eagle, and he chases after Odin all the way back to Asgard. And then when all the other gods see Odin coming, they get out some vats and Odin spits the mead back out into those vats except for a tiny little bit that he accidentally shits out his ass and it lands on the ground, and that's the mead that all the bad poets drink.

---

[57] Both *The Impudent Edda* and *The Prose Edda* provide more information about this particular myth than *The Poetic Edda*, but *The Poetic Edda*'s *Hávamál* contributes to the myth in its own small way by making it explicitly clear that Gunnlöd was emotionally distraught after being humped and dumped by Odin, as opposed to being an emotionless giantess who was only in it for the thrill of the moment and/or to get back her asshole of a dad.

Lyfjaberg Gets Taken by
Eminent Domain*

So now this part I'm going to tell you about, it all began a wicked long time ago around the time when everyone was fleeing the fucking famine in the old country. The city was just getting too fucking crowded, and the Brahmins[58] had the money to take the train up to New Hamphire and Maine to explore the mountains for picnics and skiing and shit, and so that's what they all did. And this was like a real popular thing to do that never died off, except for the railroad part as everyone just drives now instead and clogs up 93[59] like a fucking hundred-year-old toilet.

But anyway, you know, it's like Industrial fucking Revolution days, and so the Brahmins are buying up land and water rights all over the fucking place, and they're also building railroads and textile mills like there's no fucking tomorrow. And one of the side effects of all this is that there was also lots of exploration being done, too, by some old time scientist type guys since the mountains still weren't super well charted back in those days. And some of these guys started climbing up fucking Lyfjaberg itself

---

[58]   A slang term for the traditional upper class of Boston; the term is derived from a reference to the Hindu caste system.
[59]   Another mythical allusion to the fabled Interstate 93, which has previously been traversed by Kvasir in the myth, *Blood Spit Honey Death*, and Odin in the myth, *Bad Poets Drink Bird Shit*.

---

*   *This myth is the third major deviation from medieval source material found in* The Impudent Edda; *while not fully un-corroborated, its extreme departure warrants unique status.*

and making some serious fucking weather observations. Because, I mean, the weather up there really fucking sucked on account of there being a frosty old giantess who lived up there with her nine nurse goddesses.[60]

So her name's Menglad, which must have really fucking sucked for her in high school, and I don't know how she got out of Quebec[61] or convinced some goddesses to be her nurses, but she's been sitting up there waiting for her future husband to show up one day and woo her off her fucking feet because that's what's been preordained. And in the meanwhile, she's just having her nurses heal everyone who's dumb enough to hike up to the fucking summit and not propose to her. So even though all these scientists just keep showing up with broken bones and frostbite and shit, Menglad and her special nurse goddesses just keep on healing them, and everything's kind of working out in some sort of whacked out symbiotic type of way.

That is till the fucking federal government gets wind of this place and then decides they need to take the mountain over for

---

[60] While the anonymous poet of the *Codex Bostonia*'s audio-text neglected to name the nine goddesses who attend Menglad, they are revealed in *Fjölsvinnsmál*, which comprises the second half of a much older source now known as *Svipdagsmál*. The first half, *Grógaldr*, tells the story of how Svipdag performed a necromantic rite to raise the spirit of his dead mother for magical assistance on his deadly quest to visit Menglad, which had been thrust upon him by his ill-intentioned stepmother. *The Impudent Edda*'s version of this myth clearly deviates from the early sources regarding the rationale for Svigdag's visit to Lyfjaberg. In any case, according to *Svipdagsmál*, Menglad's nine goddess servants are: Hlif, Hlifthrasa, Thjodvara, Bjort, Bleik, Blid, Frid, Eir, and Aurboda.

[61] *The Impudent Edda* includes numerous instances in which Quebec is identified as an abode of giants. Unfortunately, the anonymous poet never explicitly states whether Quebec is Giant Land itself, or just some sort of frozen Giant Land satellite colony located north of New England along Yggdrasil's mid-level asymptotic luminous branch.

themselves. So they send this guy, Svipdag, up to New Hampshire on behalf of the National Weather Service to serve Menglad the notice that they're taking over the place and are going to build a fucking permanent weather station up there.[62]

So Svipdag hops on board the train, and he rides it up to Lyfjaberg, and then when he gets there, he gets off at the platform, and there's this cranky, old hobo blocking the trail up the side of the mountain. And so, naturally, the two of them get into one of those annoying question-and-answer sessions that all those fucking ancient Icelanders loved so much, and then, eventually, the old hobo figures he's heard enough bullshit about legal statutes and jurisdictional prudences and whatever the fuck else, and so he just hobbles off to wherever the hell it was he came from.[63]

So Svipdag hikes up the mountain, and, eventually, he gets to the top, and he sees this cozy little summit house where Menglad, her nurses, and some scientists are all hanging out. So he goes in, and everyone looks up at him, and Menglad sits up real straight because she notices that this guy doesn't look like just another fucking scientist and that, you know, maybe her future husband has finally fucking arrived.

And then Svipdag proceeds to give her notice that her land is being taken away by eminent domain but that she'll also be compensated for it, and she's just like, "You got to be fucking shitting me!" And so she fucking flat-out refuses to acknowledge the guy, and now it's getting real awkward at the top of Lyfjaberg, and so

---

[62] This is an important new detail for Eddic scholarship because it allows us to deduce the actual location of Lyfjaberg, which has remained elusive for centuries. While uncorroborated elsewhere, the details provided here clearly imply that Lyfjaberg was once none other than Mount Washington in the state of New Hampshire (see footnote 66 in this myth for more about Lyfjaberg's fate).

[63] *Fjölsvinnsmál* reveals that this hobo is Fjolsvid (hence the ancient poem's title). In it, he confronts Svipdag, and the two engage in a prolonged series of questions and answers. It is often presumed that Fjolsvid may be none other than Odin himself.

Mount Washington Observatory at the summit of the former Lyfjaberg in New Hampshire. The frost giantess is now gone, but the weather remains frigid and terrible.

all the scientists start to sneak out the door and back down the mountain.

So now Svipdag's all alone in there with a frost giantess and nine goddesses who all do her bidding, and let's not forget that even though Menglad's been happy enough to help heal people, she can also be fucking cruel as ice since it's in her own fucking evil giant DNA. So she tells the goddesses to lock the door, and now Svipdag's trapped in there with ten divine hostile women, and Menglad tells him that his choices are either to marry her, in which case she'll give up Lyfjaberg to the fucking Weather Service without a fight, or she and her nurses will kill him right there on the fucking spot.[64] And naturally, he's thinking he doesn't get paid

---

64 *The Impudent Edda* concurs with *Svipdagsmál* in its assertion

enough for this shit but, in the end, it was a pretty easy decision, and so he agreed to marry Menglad, and they had a super nice fucking wedding over at Bretton Woods[65] and, eventually, they moved out to Colorado where Menglad set up a new Lyfjaberg, and Svipdag got a job at the Pikes Peak Observatory.[66] And, eventually, the nurses all joined them after working at MGH[67] for a while just to make ends meet. But since they all departed, the poor Old Man of the Mountain[68] ended up crumbling down to fucking bits since there were no more divine entities to heal his wounds and keep his heart going, and so now New Hampshire's fucking state quarter don't make no fucking sense.

Honestly, I don't even know what the point of this fucking myth is. I kind of think someone just made it up.

---

that Menglad waits for her future husband to appear in the form of Svipdag. However, in *Svipdagsmál*, Svipdag is not coerced into marriage by threat of death by divine women.

[65]   The site of a historic, grand resort in the White Mountains of New Hampshire.

[66]   This is another important, new detail that augments our traditional knowledge of Eddic lore. Here, we learn that Lyfjaberg is perhaps not a permanent, geophysical location but, rather a sort of institute capable of relocation. Apparently located in New Hampshire from ancient times until the early twentieth century, Lyfjaberg appears to have been relocated to Colorado at least by the time of the recording of *The Impudent Edda*.

[67]   Shorthand for Massachusetts General Hospital in Boston.

[68]   A unique granite outcropping on Cannon Mountain that, when viewed in profile, looked like the face of an old man. Formerly the most famous attraction in the state of New Hampshire (which is somewhat sad in its own right), the Old Man was featured on the state's quarter released in the year 2000 before tragically crumbling to his rocky death in 2003.

The Night Freyja Walked the Streets

So now one night Freyja gets bored, and you know how it is, she's a girl and so she just wants to have her fun like in that Cyndi Lauper song, and so she's been hearing all the rumors flying around up in Asgard lately about all the exciting shit that's been happening out in Dwarf World, and so she decides to leave her cats at home and sneak out in the middle of the night to go check the place out for herself.[69]

Now the thing you got to realize about Freyja is, she's super fucking hot. I mean, she's so hot she can give an old blind man a boner from clear across the room. So, of course, all the guy gods want to fuck her brains out, and Odin, he wants to most of all

---

[69] It should be noted that the storyline of this myth is corroborated by neither *The Prose* nor *Poetic Edda*, and most of the sources that attest to it are only fragmentary; *The Impudent Edda* is a rare and valuable exception. The version found in *The Impudent Edda* most closely parallels that of the *Sörla þáttr* from the *Flateyjarbók*, in which Freyja commits shameful sexual acts with dwarves to obtain the necklace of her dreams. A second, less common version is also known to have existed in the *Húsdrápa*, an ancient, standalone Norse poem that has only partially survived. The remnants of that version do not describe how Freyja obtained the Brisingamen, but do make very clear that Loki has stolen it, presumably without Odin's permission. Heimdall has sought him out, and they each turn themselves into seals and engage in a sort of one-on-one special ops marine combat. Heimdall wins the fight, perhaps thinking that he might have also just won a night's worth of guilt-free sexual debauchery with Freyja for his victory and his valor.

since he's basically just a dirty, old geezer who spends most of his free time sending her dick pics. Now normally, you'd expect that type of behavior to come from someone like Loki who's a real shit prick, but the sad truth is he retired from online sexual harassment a long time ago and instead has just moved on to literally physically stalking Freyja whenever he gets the chance. Usually he wears a trench coat with nothing on underneath so that he can just jump out at her from behind the bushes and catch her by surprise while he shakes his twisted, little willy at her, but this time he's just hanging out on her property, spying on her through one of the windows all creepy-like, and so when she gets up to go and leave, he sees her and he starts to follow after her since he figures this might be a golden opportunity to do something disturbing and inappropriate.

Well, apparently, she's in a real rush and won't slow down, and so Loki ends up chasing after her all the way to fucking Dwarf World where she gets down on her hands and knees and crawls into the first shitty, late night road-side saloon that she sees. Turns out the place is mostly empty except for four thugs[70] sitting around, checking out the latest handicraft to have come out of their forges, and one of these things just so happens to be this supernatural, drop-dead gorgeous necklace called the Brisingamen. So these dwarves see Freyja at the same time she sees them, and when she catches a glimpse of that necklace, it's just fucking love at first sight for her, and so she straight-up offers the dwarves gold, silver, anything. She just has to have it.

Now these dwarves, they're some serious fucking scum, and so what they want has nothing to do with any gold or silver or any of that shit. What they want is each one of them wants to fuck Freyja. So what transpires next isn't some sort of violent dwarf on goddess assault, Jodie Foster movie-style like what went down in New Bedford back in the 80s[71] like you might think, but instead

---

[70]   The number of dwarves, or "thugs" as the poet of *The Impudent Edda* labels them, is consistent with the *Sörla þáttr*, in which they are further identified: Alfregg, Dvalin, Berling, and Grer.

[71]   This is a reference to the 1988 film, *The Accused*, which was

This pendant of Freyja from Aska, Sweden shows her entirely entwined with that which she loves the most: the Brisingamen, a tangible and extra shiny piece of jewelry.

an actual act of consensual prostitution that takes place over the course of four nights—one for each of the four fucking dwarves. And even though Freyja's got no pimp to enforce the payment, these dwarves still honor the deal anyway, and so she gets her precious Brisingamen and then goes on back home to Asgard.

Now don't forget that Loki's watching this whole fucking sordid affair as it goes down, and he's pretty fucking disgusted himself since the gods all have a serious prejudice against dwarves since they weren't very politically correct back in those days. And while Loki may be grossed out, this turn of events also presents him with an opportunity to go and tattle on Freyja to Odin, which is something that he just loves to do on those rare occassions when he isn't the one who's gone and fucked something up. So as soon as he gets back to Asgard, he rushes over to Odin's place and tells him all about it, and Odin just completely fucking flips out, since he's jealous, you know. I mean, the guy's been hitting on Freyja ever since she went to live in Asgard as part of

loosely based on a real-life incident in New Bedford, Massachusetts that involved a horrific sexual assault by the worst sort of human scum imaginable.

the truce to end the war of the gods that started when Odin murdered that damned witch.[72] But she's never really been into him since he's way older than her, only's got one eye, and perhaps most importantly, he's kind of socially fucking awkward. So all she ever does is ignore him, and now when he finds out she's willing to give it up to any dwarf with a gold necklace, it just sets him off, and once he calms his liver, he sends Loki back on over to Freyja's place and tells him to steal the necklace since she doesn't deserve to have it on account of how she got it.

And you know how Loki is, he enjoys commiting felonies so he jumps at the opportunity, and so when he gets back over to Freyja's place, he turns himself into a tiny fucking fly, flies into her house, bites her on the fucking neck out of spite, and then turns back into his normal self so as to be able to steal the necklace. And then he sneaks back out of the house without her ever even waking up. So the next morning Freyja notices that the Brisingamen's missing and gets real pissed, but she also realizes that only Loki is a talented enough thief to be able to pull off something like that, but she also realizes that even he wouldn't dare do such a thing in Asgard without Odin's express permission. So she marches straight over to Odin's house, raising high hell, and demanding to know just what the fuck is going on. And Odin being the top god just tells her to shut the fuck up and go start a war on Middle-Earth if she ever wants to see her fucking necklace again.[73]

War and death usually put the old creeper in a good mood.

---

[72]   Regarding Odin's murder of the witch and the ambiguity surrounding Freyja's potential role in the incident, see footnote 21 in the myth, *How Not to Get Away with Witch Murder*.

[73]   Unlike *The Impudent Edda*, the *Sörla þáttr* continues on the trajectory this topic, describing at great length the epic war and misery among men caused by Freyja's war-mongering at the behest of Odin. While Snorri may not give us much to work with regarding the origins of the Brisingamen itself, he does give us a brief overview of this period of strife and the everlasting battle between the kings Hethin and Högni in *The Prose Edda*'s *Skáldskaparmál*.

Frey's Inglorious Gay Bar Experience*

All right, so it's been a shitty ass week and it's finally fucking Friday, and so, of course, Frey can't wait to start drinking like a fucking horse which is what he does every Friday since it's his special day of the week and all.[74] So as soon as he gets off of work, he goes down to the local bar where he normally meets his buddies, and he proceeds to get fucking shitfaced.

So now he's sitting there at the bar, knocking back his pints of Sam Adams like there's no tomorrow and wondering where the fuck everyone else is. So, eventually, he gets a text from Thor, and it turns out he can't make it since he's having to leave town for work again since there's some trolls on the loose that need to be murdered, and Frey just figures Loki's going to be late like always since he's a dick, and sure enough that's what happens.

So Loki finally shows up and, right off the bat, he sees Frey's already pretty far gone, and so he goes up to him and asks him where Thor is, and Frey's just like, "Yeah, you know, I don't know, I guess his dad made him go on a trip to kill some more trolls or

---

[74] Four of the seven days of the week are named after the Norse gods in the modern Germanic languages, including English. These are Tuesday (Tyr's Day), Wednesday (Woden's Day; Woden is the Anglo-Saxon cognate for Odin); Thursday (Thor's Day), and Friday (Frey/Freyja/Frigg's Day).

* *This myth is the fourth of nine found in* The Impudent Edda *that is not attested to in either of the Elder Eddas or other medieval source material.*

something again this weekend, so he ain't going to make it out tonight." And Loki, being the devious piece of shit that he is, immediately starts thinking about all the different ways he can fuck with Frey tonight and get away with it thanks to Thor not being there to stick up for him and all.

So first thing he does is he orders a fucking pitcher and starts filling up Frey's glass. But he himself, he barely even touches it, and so he just watches Frey basically down the entire fucking pitcher by himself. And you got to understand here that Frey's no Thor when it comes to drinking, and so when they get up to leave, he can barely even fucking stand straight, and so now you got Loki leading Frey outside by the hand, and they start walking down the street, and Frey's got no idea where the fuck they're going but, eventually, they get somewhere, and they go inside, and then Loki just fucking disappears. So now Frey's wandering around looking for fucking Loki who's nowhere to be found, and so he starts thinking, "Well, maybe Loki went into the men's room," so he makes his way over there but sure enough, Loki's not in the men's room, either, but a bunch of dudes all dressed in black leather with shaved chests are, and so he thinks, "That's kind of odd but whatever." He figures, you know, maybe it's some sort of crazy Dwarf World theme night or something.

So he leaves the men's room, and he starts looking for Loki on the dance floor, and then he starts wondering, "Hey, where're all the chicks?" And then at that exact same moment that song "Hungry Like the Wolf" comes on over the PA, and the fucking crowd goes wild, and then some of these guys start getting up real close and fucking grinding on Frey and commenting on his package since he's fucking huge in that regard,[75] and all of sudden

---

[75]   As the foremost fertility god of the Vanir, Frey was frequently associated with both male libido and the harvest of crops. Because of this, his woody member has always been held in very high esteem; it has historically received more special attention than any other Norse god's willy. Thus, it is not surprising that

Is this a god? A feathered miscreant (likely a divine being under the influence of extreme transmogrification) searches the gutter for personal items that Frey may have lost while sleeping it off.

that's when it dawns on him, and he realizes the shit that Loki just pulled on his sorry ass, and so he runs off the dance floor and then back out into the street where he spews his fucking guts out since he's so fucking drunk and his sensitive-ass stomach just can't take the sudden motion.

And he doesn't know what happened next, but some nice guy must have called him a cab or something because he woke up in the bushes outside his place with his keys in a puddle of puke in the fucking gutter.

---

he attracted the covetous eyes of multiple customers at the venue in which he found himself in the present myth. Nor is it surprising that Loki specifically chose him to be the butt of this prank, although had Thor been in town and not away smashing his hammer on trolls, he might very well have been duped into the same scenario as Frey. For more on Frey's indomitable manhood, please see the myth, *Sad, Flaccid Sex God.*

Loki is a Dead-Beat Dad

Now getting back to Loki. So his father was a fucking giant, and so, you know, it's like, what do you fucking expect? Evil just runs in his genes and trying to make a good guy out of him's about as likely as the Kennedy family going Republican—it just ain't going to fucking happen. But somehow he managed to get Sigyn to marry him—yeah, go figure—and together they had this kid Nari or Narfi[76] or something, which sounds kind of like some bullshit from *Pinky and the Brain* but whatever. He's their kid not mine.

But Loki, he's not a faithful husband—I mean at this point, he's already slept with Thor's wife and had sex with a horse, and that's only the dirty laundry we even fucking know about! So it's not really all that surprising when he goes one day and fucks some ogress[77] out in the woods, and he ends up getting her knocked up with triplets. And why he didn't wear a rubber, I got no idea.

But anyway, that fucking ogress pops out some little bastards nine months later, and they all turn out to be some of the ugliest

---

[76] The poet of *The Impudent Edda* is not the first Eddic scribe to have confused the identity of Loki's son or sons. Snorri was similarly confused many centuries ago when he apparently lacked certainty about the son's specific name in the *Gylfaginning*, while *The Poetic Edda*'s *Lokasenna* instead asserts that Narfi and Nari were two distinct sons of Loki. This is made very clear in a prose accompaniment to *Lokasenna* in which Nari is gutted by the gods and Narfi is transformed into a wolf, which is also described later in this volume in the myth, *Snake Poison Torture Time*.

[77] *The Prose Edda* identifies this ogress as Angrboda.

babies the world has ever even seen. And being as their dad is who he is, they're also rotten to the fucking core. So the first one's a wolf, the second one's a snake, and the last one's some sort of fucking demon woman.

Now the rest of the gods, they find out about these ugly bastards, and then they start hearing all these prophecies about how they're some real bad eggs that were all conceived under the sign of some wicked bad norn and that all three are going to grow up to be even worse than a couple of Chechan dipshits from Cambridge[78] which is kind of hard to believe, but that's what the prophecies are saying. And so Odin, he doesn't take this kind of shit lightly, so he sends his guys to go and pick these freaks up and bring them on back to Asgard.

So they're back in Asgard now, and the first thing Odin does is he grabs a hold of the snake, and he fucking chucks the monster as far out into the middle of the North Atlantic as he can in the hopes that it'll fucking drown to death, but instead it just starts to grow bigger and bigger and bigger till finally it encircles the whole wide world, and then it starts biting itself on its own tail since it's fucking retarded since snakes don't have much brains.[79]

And well, obviously that didn't work out so well, so instead of attemping to toss that demon woman out into the middle of the ocean, too, he just banishes her down to Hel, which is also her name.[80] She's real creepy and has some sort of fucked

---

[78] This is a reference to the detestable 2013 Boston Marathon bombers: the brothers, Tamerlan Tsarnaev and Dzhokhar Tsarnaev.
[79] While the serpent goes unnamed at this point in *The Impudent Edda*, it is clear that it is none other than Jörmundgandr, the notorious Middle-Earth serpent.
[80] The location of Hel's domain of Hel is situated within the asymptotic giant branch of Yggdrasil that lies closest to the long-duration gamma-ray burst known as Níðhöggr the Dragon. It remains unknown specifically what sort of effects Níðhöggr the Dragon's residual cosmic radiation has on the inhabitants of Hel. However, the Old Norse scientific community has generally

Landscape in the vicinity of the Kancamagus Highway in the White Mountains of New Hampshire. A well-known scenic byway frequently visited by Tyr and his copilot-is-dog/wolf/ monster buddy, Fenrir, back when the world was still young.

up dermatological demarcation running across her body, segregating her skin color so that she's as pale as any white Irish ass up on top but she's fucking black as coal like a Somalian down below the waist. And man, is she one volatile bitch. If you don't die in battle and get to go up to Odin's hall up high in the sky where you get to feast and fight till the end of time, then you have to go straight down to Hel and suffer till the huge fucking fire at the end of time finally just puts you out of your misery.

---

agreed that if a study of systematic observation were ever to be undertaken, the Dragon's rate of isotopic decay would exhibit such weak behavior that little or no effect would be discernable among Hel's inhabitants.

But as for Fenrir—that's the fucking wolf—the gods actually didn't think he was so bad at first. Hell, they even let him stay on at Asgard for a while, and, you know, he was kind of like their pet dog. And Tyr in particular, he got to be real fond of old Fenrir. He'd go and he'd feed Fenrir on a regular basis because they were buddies back then. Fuck, he'd even take the top off of his Jeep, and he'd put Fenrir up in the front seat, and then they'd go for a ride up along the Kancamagus Highway[81] just to check out the fall foliage. It was just real normal stuff that they'd do together like that, and Tyr, he didn't even have to worry about Fenrir jumping out of the car and losing a fucking leg or anything because Fenrir, you know, he had human intelligence, and so he could even talk and shit. And so they'd just be cruising along around the backroads, blasting classic rock tunes as the wind blew in their hair, and maybe they'd take a break and have a few beers or something before heading back into town at the end of the day.[82]

---

[81] The Kancamagus Highway is a renowned scenic road through the White Mountains of New Hampshire.

[82] *The Impudent Edda* shines a very different light on Tyr and Fenrir's relationship in the early days than is depicted in *The Prose Edda*'s *Gylfaginning*. In *The Prose Edda*, Tyr is described as the only god brave enough to face the wolf during feeding time, and that he most definitely did not take the wolf along as his co-pilot when out cruising on nice, sunny days with clear, blue skies.

Divine Hands Make
Good Wolf Fodder

So the thing is, the rest of the gods, they don't care much for the fact that Tyr's been going around and hanging out so much with this damn wolf. Now I don't know if they're all just a bunch of cat people or what the fuck their problem is, but they were always kind of scared of Fenrir anyway because, like I said before, basically, there's this prophecy out there that says the fucking animal's eventually going to completely flip the fuck out one day and eat Odin alive.

So Odin and all his guys, they finally decide it's about time to take Fenrir out on account of this prophecy, which in a way might make it a sort of self-fulfilling one, but who knows? But, anyway, so the gods, they go and they get these special collars, and then they try to trick Fenrir into putting them on around his neck[83] in the hopes that he won't get loose and break out of them so that they'd then be able to go and lock him up wherever they fucking felt like. It was like a dare, you know? Odin'd be like "Hey Fenrir, bet you can't break out of this here iron collar."

And Fenrir, since he's a highly irritable animal, and truth be told is pretty much a total fucking dick to everyone except Tyr, he'd be like, "Hey Odin, go fuck yourself." And then he'd go and

---

83 The notion of collars being placed around the wolf's neck is a unique and special detail that has evolved since the *The Prose Edda*'s *Gylfaginning*'s narrative about this myth was initially recorded. In that version, the wolf is instead bound with a series of fetters around his leg(s).

The islands of Casco Bay as viewed from Portland, Maine. It has been prophesied that at Ragnarök, Fenrir will break loose from his captivity on one of these islands and go on a wild and senseless killing spree as revenge for having been taunted for so long with dog treats that were just always barely beyond his reach.

he'd take a fucking dump right there in the middle of the carpet, and Tyr'd have to go and clean it up. But Odin knows Fenrir's got a weak spot for Milkbones, so he'd go and he'd get one out of the box, and he'd tell the wolf that he'll give it to him if he just puts his head through the fucking collar. And, naturally, Fenrir's got no pride when it comes to doing dumb tricks for treats, so he sticks his head into the collar and he flexes his neck muscles, and he breaks the fucking thing like it was a fucking paper doily. So Odin gives Fenrir the Milkbone, and he fucking scarfs the thing down, and everyone seems all happy and shit on the outside, but on the inside they're getting real fucking nervous because they're starting to think they aren't going to be able to contain this animal after all.

So Odin, being the sneaky bastard that he is, he sends this other guy, Skirnir, off to Dwarf World since that place is about as lawless as Juarez on New Year's Eve, and you can pretty much get anything there. So Skirnir's supposed to find some real fucking diminutive thugs who'll make him a magical collar to bind Fenrir's punk ass with, and pretty soon he finds some that are willing to do business with him, and they proceed to make a binding that's made out of some real fucked up shit.[84]

So next, the gods go and they take Fenrir out to some island off the coast of Maine for a nice summer getaway, and so they're all there now, hanging out by the water and daring each other to do stupid shit, and sooner or later Odin finally dares the animal to put this new binding around his neck and to try and break out of it again like last time. Only this time Fenrir looks at this thing, and he's like, "What the fuck is that? It looks like a fucking ribbon." Because it did look like a fucking ribbon, so, naturally, it made him suspicious. I mean, this special dwarf-made collar looked more like a flimsy scarf than an iron-forged mechanism used for testing hardcore feats of neck strength.

But the gods, you know, they just kept at it till, eventually, that one-eyed suiciding freak himself just offered up an entire fucking box of Milkbones, and for Fenrir, that's just way too good an offer to pass up, and so he gives in, but he also makes a couple of extra demands first. So he tells them, "First, if it turns out this is some sort of magical device like I suspect it is, and I can't get out of it, then you got to set me free. And second, as a fucking re-

---

84   While the poet of *The Impudent Edda* completely neglects the details of what this "real fucked up shit" is, Snorri divulges in *The Prose Edda* that the materials used in the manufacture of Gleipnir (the name of the final ribbon-like binding) are the following: the noise that a cat's footsteps make, a woman's beard, the roots of a mountain, the muscle tendons of a bear, a fish's breath, and bird spit.

assurance to your good will, one of you needs to put your fucking hand in my mouth while we do this thing, because I know you're all a bunch of fucking liars and cheaters, and this way at least I'll get to bite someone's fucking hand off if you're all trying to trick me. And in any case, I still get all the fucking Milkbones."

And so the gods all look over at Tyr since he and the wolf'd always been buddies, and Tyr's just like, "Ah, fuck."

So he goes and he sticks his right hand in Fenrir's fucking mouth, and then the gods go and they put the ribbon around Fenrir's neck and tell him to give it a shot, and as soon as he starts trying to break free, the ribbon just gets tighter and tighter and it just won't fucking break. And so those fucking gods man, they all just started cracking up. They thought this shit was fucking hilarious, except for poor Tyr who just got his hand bitten off and is now wandering around in a daze looking for some fucking Tylenol.

And now at this point, Fenrir's figured out that the gods pretty much fucked him over, and so he's fucking pissed and he's going fucking berserk, and so what the gods do is they take the other end of the ribbon, and they leash it around this huge ass boulder so that he can't go anywhere, and then they set the box of Milkbones down on the ground just out of his reach just to really fuck with him.[85] So now Fenrir's stuck there, staring at a box full of dog treats that he can't even reach, and drooling like a bitch till the end of the world when he's finally going to break free, eat all the fucking Milkbones, and then go and eat Odin alive out of revenge right before the rest of the universe goes up in flames.

---

[85]   The use of dog treats (official Milkbone brand or otherwise) in the binding of Fenrir is a relatively late development that is only attested to in *The Impudent Edda*'s rendition of this particular myth. Their use in taunting Fenrir after successfully binding him has also subsumed the older tradition of torture that Snorri relates in *The Prose Edda* in which the gods instead lodge a sword in Fenrir's mouth, wedging its hilt in his lower gums and its point in his upper gums, causing him to drool, just as the barely out-of-reach Milkbones do in *The Impudent Edda*.

Never Go Apple-Picking
with a Bad God

All right, so one day Odin and Loki and Hoenir are up in New Hampshire hiking because why the fuck not? Except I don't know why they brought Hoenir along with them since he doesn't do shit.[86] But whatever.

So anyway, these guys, they get hungry so they go and gut a fucking ox out there in the middle of fucking nowhere, and then they build a fucking fire to roast the thing on, only the meat's not getting any warmer. So they near about get into a brawl over this and scare off all the other campers when some damn eagle sitting in the tree next to them starts mouthing off like some sort of demented cartoon character. So this eagle, he says, "Hey, you shitheads, you want your meat to cook? Well, then you better share some of it with me otherwise that fire's never going to heat up."

So the gods are all like, "Yeah, all right, go and get the fire started, you crazy fucking talking animal." And before you know it, they got a nice fire going, and the ox's cooking and the meat's just about ready to fall off the fucking bone when that eagle

---

[86] The role of Hoenir has traditionally been ambiguous and inconsistent through the ages and the extant sources, as first mentioned in footnote 10 of the myth, *Middle-Earth is Just an Eyelash on the Celestial Gallows Pole*. Additionally, it is unclear why Hoenir would be traveling with Odin and Loki, rather than his companions among the Vanir after he got traded to them as part of the deal that ended the war of the gods that resulted when Odin murdered a witch, as described in the myth, *How Not to Get Away with Witch Murder*.

swoops down from out of the branches and fucking eats half of it before anyone even knows what happened!

So, of course, Loki loses his shit right then and there and starts chasing this damned bird all over the campsite with a fucking stick, trying to smack the living shit out of it, but then the fucking thing grabs hold of the stick and takes off, carrying Loki with him, and so now Loki's getting his ass dragged all over the place, getting banged up against tons of shit like pop-up trailers and picnic tables and outhouses till finally they end up out on 93,[87] at which point he starts to develop a real fucking acute case of road rash since he's too fucking stupid to let go.

So now the damn bird's gaining in altitude and threatening to smash Loki's face into the side of the fucking mountain, which he's had lots of practice with doing to other dipshits over the years. And so now at this point, Loki just starts begging for his fucking life, and the bird's like, "Yeah, I'll let you live, but you're going to have to get Idunn to walk out of Asgard with her magical special apples for me if I let you go."

And so, of course, Loki agrees to this since he's a filthy fucking sack of shit. But he doesn't say anything about his dirty under-handed deal when he gets back to the campsite, and Odin and Hoenir are still rolling on the ground laughing their asses off about how he got the shit kicked out of him by a talking bird.

Anyway, they have their dinner, or whatever's left of it at least, and then the next day they head on back to Asgard. And things are normal for a while, but then one day Loki goes over to Idunn's house, and he tells her he's seen this orchard full of wicked juicy apples right outside of Asgard and that she ought to come along with him to see if they can try and graft some of her apples onto them so as to make an all-new kind of super awesome apple tree. Well, Idunn lives for this shit, and she's

---

[87] Once again, U.S. Interstate 93 makes a highly conspicuous, yet meaningful mythological appearance in *The Impudent Edda*.

*A typical northern New England camping scene, much like
the one at which the gods failed to roast their meat without
the assistance of an evil, talking bird...so much smoke, but
so little edible food.*

gullible as hell, so she gets in Loki's beat-up old Pinto with her
basket of magical apples, and they head out of town together.

So they cruise on over the rainbow bridge, and they get to
the orchard Loki'd been talking about, and all the fucking fam-
ilies have already practically picked the place fucking clean, but
Loki sees a tree that looks semi-decent so he tells Idunn to go
check it out while he goes inside to get hammered on fruit wine.
So Idunn's out there now, checking out the apple tree and wondering what the big fucking deal was, when all of a sudden that
same damned talking eagle swoops down from out of fucking
nowhere and picks her up with its pointy fucking toenails and
carries her off all the way back to Quebec.[88]

---

[88]   *The Impudent Edda* is the first primary source to assert that

So now the rest of the gods are going, "Where the fuck's Idunn?" Because they need to eat some of her fucking apples so as to stay young, since that's what they're for. They're special apples of youth or some shit, and even though Odin's old as fuck, he still gets around pretty good thanks to these apples. Well, the gods weren't born yesterday, and they remember Idunn getting into Loki's crappy old shit-mobile so they start to interrogate his ass, and sure enough, he coughs up the truth and receives a collective death threat from all the rest of the gods that if he doesn't bring Idunn and her apples back damn soon, then they're going to fucking flay him alive.

So now Loki's got no choice but to ask Freyja if he can borrow her special magical shape changing costume, and she's like, "Yeah, sure," so he takes this thing and he puts it on and transforms himself into a fucking falcon,[89] and next thing you know he's

---

Thjazi's home is in Quebec (the anonymous poet reveals the identity of the eagle as Thjazi on the next page). See footnote 61 in the myth, *Lyfjaberg Gets Taken by Eminent Domain*, for more about Quebec's ambiguous role as a stronghold of evil.

[89] It is unclear why Loki, who clearly possesses the ability to spontaneously break his own symmetry and manipulate his own constituent god particles (as first witnessed with his transformation into a horse in the myth, *Loki Gets Boned by a Horse*, and again in his transformation into a fly in the myth, *The Night Freyja Walked the Streets*) would need to borrow someone else's god particle altering device, also known as a transmogrifier. It is plausible that Loki never fully achieved the advanced ability to reach a state of quantum excitation equivalent to the form of a falcon, hence his need to borrow Freyja's transmogrifier. It should be noted that Freyja's device only offered its user the ability to alter the mass of their god particles into the specific form of a falcon, rather than a full range of forms, and as such was quite possibly just an early-model transmogrifier with limited transmogrification capacity. The concept of the transmogrifier was first theorized in the late 20th century by a duo of experimental scientists who, wishing to keep their true identities secret, signed

bypassing the TSA strip-search and flying nonstop all they way up to French-fucking-Canadia. Around about this time, it dawns on him that the eagle was none other than the evil giant, Thjazi, since the gods never realize they're dealing with giants till they've already fucked something up, and then it hits them.

Stupid as shit, but that's the way it goes.

So Loki flies straight to Thjazi's house and sees that the guy's not home as he's taken his boat out onto the river, so Loki breaks and enters as tends to be his habit, and he finds Idunn locked in the basement with her apples, and then he transforms her into a nut[90] since this is apparently one of his special skills—turning people into nuts that is—and so he grabs her up by his falcon talons and flies her ass straight back to Asgard.

Well, Thjazi's out in his boat when he happens to look up into the sky, and he sees this falcon flying overhead carrying a nut in its one foot, and he's like, "You got to be fucking kidding me!" Since he has a special sixth sense that lets him know when someone he's kidnapped has been turned into a nut. So now he turns himself back into an eagle, and he flies after Loki, and he's

---

their work using the pseudonymous names of two prominent 16th and 17th century philosophers.

[90] While the standard model of particle physics has been used to explain the resultant state of mass and degree of symmetry that results when certain gods elevate their own constituent god particles to a state of quantum excitation, less has been theorized about their ability to project such invisible and difficult-to-detect forces on the god particles of others. Some members of the scientific community, however, have postulated that Loki, by unknown means, came into possession of a rare, full-range capacity cosmic transmogrifier, which he uses in this instance to transform Idunn into a nut. This would be consistent with Loki's actions, as he needed to preserve his own personal full-range capacity transmogrifier for use on Idunn, therefore necessitating his reliance on Freyja's limited-capacity transmogrifier to transform himself into a falcon, since it is believed that transmogrifiers may only be used on one subject at a time.

getting damn near catching up with Loki, and they're right outside of Asgard, and it's looking like it's about to turn into some
sort of straight-up *Top Gun*-style bird-on-bird combat shit in the
sky, but then Thor gets out his flame-thrower,[91] takes aim till he
has missile-lock, and then he just fucking torches that fucking
eagle to a goddamned crisp.[92] And then when the carcass crashes
to the ground, all the other gods run over and start stabbing the
shit out of it with their own weapons just for good measure. It
was fucking awesome!

---

[91] This is the first and only instance among all of the surviving
sources of Norse mythology in which Thor's flame-thrower makes
an appearance. Sadly, its name has been lost to the mists of time.
[92] The killing of Thjazi is a highly-acclaimed event in Norse
mythology, and the particulars of his death have evolved rather
dramatically from the incident's appearance in the *Skáldskaparmál* of *The Prose Edda*. In that rendition, rather than Thor pulling
out his flame-thrower, or even his hammer, to kill the giant as was
his custom, the gods instead collectively gathered some kindling,
placed it atop the walls of Asgard, and then lit all of it on fire at
the exact moment when Thjazi was flying by (Loki having already
made it safely past the walls). Thjazi's wings caught on fire, and
he crashed to the ground, injured but alive. The gods then rushed
over to where he lay and mercilessly slaughtered him on the
spot. Conversely, in *The Poetic Edda*'s *Hárbarðsljóð*, Thor claims
to have done the killing of Thjazi himself during his prolonged
verbal dispute over the availability of river-crossing services with
the cantankerous old ferryman, Harbard, who is really just Odin
in disguise. Thor isn't the brightest bulb on the block and in this
instance fails to realize that his dad is just messing with him.

The Mistreatment of a
Deviant's Ballsack

So now Thjazi's deader than a door nail, and his daughter Ska-di's wondering where the fuck he went off to, and when he still doesn't come home for a number of days, she begins to suspect that the gods probably murdered his ass since that's by far the number one cause of disappearances up in Giant Land. So she gets on her war gear and heads down to Asgard herself to get some fucking revenge.

So she gets there, and Odin pretty much confirms her suspicions that her dad got killed, but then he kind of had it coming to him anyway since he kidnapped Idunn in the first place with the help of that traitor, Loki, but Skadi doesn't care about any of that and threatens to go fucking berserk if she doesn't get some sort of recompense, and so Odin's like, "Well, what do you want, you crazy fucking bitch?"

And Skadi says she wants to marry one of the gods, to which Odin's like, "Yeah, that's fine, but only on the condition that you pick him out based on the appearance of his feet." And so she agrees, and then all the dude gods line up and cover up all their bodies and faces except for their feet, and so Skadi's eyeing these guys up and down and finally finds this pair of beautiful feet, and she figures this guy must be Brady[93] since

---

[93] Traditionally, in all other sources, this god has been identi-fied as Balder, son of Odin and half brother of Thor, and con-sistently portrayed as the most attractive and well-meaning of the gods. In the centuries that have elapsed since the writing of

Brady's so damned good looking, he's got to have the best feet of the bunch too, right?

WRONG! Those feet belong to Njord, who's an ancient mariner and even though, so far as I know, he's not cursed since he never shot down no fucking albatross, it doesn't really matter any because Skadi's heartbroken since she wanted to marry the hot god with the golden arm, not the salty, old sea-dog. So now she declares that she'll never laugh ever again for so long as they both shall live. Now for whatever reason, the one-eyed freak actually gives a shit about her emotional well-being, which is a real rarity on his part, but he works in mysterious ways so whatever, and so he commands Loki, who's still largely to blame for this whole mess, to make her laugh so that she'll go away and stop bothering them.

Well, Loki's a real perverse mother-fucker so he strips down bare-ass naked, and he goes and he gets some thin rope that he then lassos around his ballsack, and then he ties the other end of it to the beard of the nearest fucking goat. Next, he proceeds to play the sickest game of tug of war that the world's ever fucking seen. But this is exactly the type of shit the gods think is hilarious, so they're all cracking up, but Skadi's uptight as it gets so she's just sitting there sulking, but then the goat stops tugging on his end of the rope since he doesn't want to have all his facial

---

the Elder Eddas and other early source material, his physical appearance—particularly pertaining to his style of dress—and name have morphed and coalesced with the foremost present-day deity of New England (prior to his defection to Florida, that is). *The Impudent Edda*'s fusion of the older, iconically Scandinavian tradition of Balder with the more recent, distinctively Bostonian tradition of Tom Brady is an unsurprising mythological evolution. Historically, substantial and prolonged exposure to the customs and beliefs of different cultures has resulted in the adaptation and subsumption by the prevailing mythological beliefs of the lesser ones, and as explained in the Introduction, such mythological beliefs have never existed in a completely immutable stasis anyway.

hair ripped off his face, and so, all of a sudden, Loki slips and
falls straight into Skadi's lap, and she finally laughs, just a little. And then to help ease matters over even more, Odin gouges
Thjazi's eyes out of his skull and then throws them up into the
sky where they become stars.

So now that Skadi's finally satisfied, she and Njord go back to
Quebec but Njord fucking hates French so they leave after nine
days and go back to his place in Asgard, but Skadi doesn't like living near the water so she leaves him and goes on back to Quebec,[94]
and they basically live apart in a highly dysfunctional marriage but
neither of them cares enough to bother with filing for a fucking
divorce, and I guess the norns just kind of dropped the ball on
ending that one with any sort of sense of finality.

---

[94] *The Impudent Edda* deviates from earlier sources in its description of the homes of Njord and Skadi, as well as the reasons
for why their marriage failed. The *Gylfaginning* in *The Prose Edda*
makes it clear that Njord hated Skadi's home of Thrymheim because it was extremely wintery and cold (like Quebec) but also
mountainous and full of wolves (less like Quebec). Skadi hated
Njord's shipyard-like home of Noatun because of the commotion
of port life and the squealing of the gulls. In general, because
she married into the family of the Aesir, she became related to
them. Consequently, she stopped being a simple, lowly giantess
and daughter of the evil-hearted Thjazi, and instead became the
wondrous ski goddess of winter and very popular in Vermont.

Tyr Enters a Mosh Pit*

Now the thing that not everyone knows about Tyr is that he's a total fucking metalhead[95] and that he especially likes the shit that deals lyrically with vikings and ancient pagan deities and sacrificial rites and whatnot, which figures since, you know, he's an ancient viking god of war himself. Just kind of goes hand-in-hand with the whole territory even though he's only got one hand himself since he let his favorite pet eat the other one.

But Tyr, he's been into metal ever since his grandma grew her nine-hundredth head.[96] Before she grew that final head, he'd only been into swords, spears, knives, fucking war hammers, maces, shit like that in terms of metal—pretty much anything made out of metal that could be used to kill someone with. It was a real morbid fucking fascination. But then his grandma popped her nine-hundredth head into existence, and he just couldn't take all the grand-motherly smothering coming at him from nine-hundred different

---

[95] The anonymous poet's assertion that Tyr is a metalhead has not been corroborated by any other source.

[96] Very little is known about how Tyr's grandmother managed to grow nine-hundred heads or at what rate she grew them, but the assertion here that she did not grow them all at once is an important new detail that expands upon the information previously provided by *The Poetic Edda's Hymiskviða*.

---

* *This myth is the fifth of nine found in* The Impudent Edda *that is not attested to in either of the Elder Eddas or other medieval source material.*

fucking directions all at once, and so he went and he locked himself
in his room, and before you know it, he was listening to Sabbath
and trying to learn to play guitar, which I guess he was actually
pretty good at back when he still had two fucking hands.

Tyr's actually a big fan of Def Leppard, too, for obvious fucking reasons.

But his most favorite bands are the ones that have been doing
the whole viking and folk metal type of thing the last few decades.
I mean, ever since Quorthon[97] figured out how to invent viking
metal music, Tyr's been listening to them all, including everything tangentially related, too. I mean, he listens to Bathory and
Enslaved and Helheim and Einherjer and Thyrfing and Moonsor-
row and Borknagar and Falkenbach and Ásmegin and Ensiferum
and Glittertind and Heidevolk and Wardruna and Månegarm and
Fejd and Metsatöll and Skálmöld and Turisas and Unleashed and
Amon Amarth and Grand Magus and Wintersun and Heilung
and Myrkur and Korpiklaani and Pagan Altar and Finntroll and
Battle Ruins and Varjagikaarti and the list just goes on and on.[98]
But naturally, Tyr's most favorite fucking metal band is Týr from
the Faroe fuckin' Islands, and wouldn't you know it, but he finds
out they're coming to fucking Worcester![99]

---

[97] Thomas Börje Forsberg, better known as Quorthon, was a
Swedish musician and the creative genius behind the band, Bathory. He is generally regarded as the all-father of the viking metal musical subgenre.

[98] Here, the anonymous poet utilizes a traditional Norse literary device, known as a thula, that involves listing the names of a
certain category of people, places, or things simply for the sake of
listing them. A particularly well-known example is the *Dvergatal*
from *Völuspá*, in which a very large number of dwarves are named
one by one. *The Impudent Edda* also includes one other notable
instance of a thula. Known as *The Lay of the Bs*, this set of stanzas
has been edited out of the main body of text of this edition due
to its irrelevance, but may be found reproduced in the Appendix.

[99] Worcester is the second largest city in the state of Massachu-

So he gets in his car and he drives out to fucking Worcester, which he's really good at even though he only has one hand and he's driving a standard. And so he gets there, and he parks his car over on some shady side street so he doesn't have to pay for parking, and then he walks his ass on over to the Palladium.[100] And the guy isn't exactly incon-fucking-spicuous, you know? Like, the fucking streets are pretty empty to begin with since this is downtown Worcester after dark on a Tuesday night after all, and the place is a fucking shithole. And all the people who're loitering around outside of the Palladium are mostly all dressed in black with their leather jackets and band shirts and shit. But then you get Tyr who walks up to the place wearing nothing but military boots, leather pants, and a fucking bear skin hat/cape thing. But you know, he's got his ticket, and so they pat him down, and they let him on in, and he goes straight back to the lower bar, and he begins to get liquored up while the opening band plays, whoever they are. No one remembers.

And then Týr comes out on stage, and they open with their song "Gates of Hel," and, holy fucking shit, does Tyr go nuts. I mean, so does the whole audience, but especially Tyr. He roars at the top of his lungs, spitting out beer, which makes him look like he's foaming at the fucking mouth. And then he starts to head-bang, and everyone moves away from him because no one wants to get smashed in the face by some crazy headbanger who's wearing a fucking bear skull on top of his head.

And then pretty soon the mosh pit starts up. It swirls around for a bit, kind of low-key, you know, and then it just fucking explodes once Týr starts playing "Blood of Heroes." And now Tyr can't refrain anymore, and so he enters the mosh pit now him-

---

setts, as well as all of New England, and lies about one hour west of Boston. Speakers of the local dialect pronounce the city's name approximately as "Woostah."

100   The Palladium is a live music venue located in downtown Worcester. It hosts the majority of Massachusetts' metal concerts.

The Palladium in Worcester, Massachusetts, where Tyr was once forcefully removed from a Týr concert for inappropriate and overly aggressive, violent behavior.

self, and so he's in there now, charging against all the other guys, bouncing off them, waving his stump around up in the air high above his bear skull hat, and the whole damn time he's still holding onto his fucking beer with his one good hand!

And then he climbs the stage to do a stage dive, and they catch him and all, and everyone's having a good time, and then the song ends, and Týr starts to play "The Lay of Our Love," which is one of their slower ballads so everyone calms down a bit. Everyone except Tyr that is, as he tries to keep the fucking mosh going, but no one else wants it during this sobering song of loss and death, and so now it's starting to become a scene, and the bouncers are closing in on Tyr but he's in total fucking berserker mode and snarling like a fucking beast. And well, Týr sees the drama unfolding from up on stage, and so the drummer throws one of his sticks at Tyr, and it hits him square in the fucking face, and it stuns him enough that four of the bouncers are able to tackle him, and then they drag him outside, and they toss him and his animal pelt out onto the fucking street and then they go back inside.

So now Tyr stands up and he tries to go back in but the doors are locked, and after a bit of pointless commotion, he calms his liver and realizes he's too fucking drunk to drive home, and so he calls Odin to see if he can come and pick him up, but Odin's down in Mimir's cave sending dick pics to Freyja, and so he refuses to answer his phone. So now Tyr's forced to call Thor to get a ride instead, which kind of pisses Thor off since he's having a rare quiet night off from killing trolls and shit and, you know, he's just sitting there watching *Bridesmaids*, which is one of his most favorite fucking movies of all time since it's one that he really relates to.[101]

But anyway, Thor goes and he gets his goats out of the fucking garage, and then when he shows up in Worcester, he can hear Týr playing "Hail to the Hammer" inside the Palladium, and even though Thor's more of a Bee Gees and Ace of Base kind of guy himself, that song just speaks straight to his fucking soul, and so he rips off one of the outter doors, and he goes inside while Tyr sits down on the curb and starts puking his fucking brains out.

---

[101] See the next myth, *Thor's Cross-Dressing Misadventure*, for more information about Thor's general interest in bridal parties.

Thor's Cross-Dressing Misadventure

So this one day Thor wakes up and his fucking hammer's fucking missing,[102] which is real fucked up because usually he sleeps with it like it's a security blanket, and so, of course, he gets super pissed and goes straight on over to Loki's house to bitch and complain about it since they have a weird, unhealthy sort of dependent relationship, and then Loki's like, "Let's go over to Freyja's place to see if she'll let us borrow her falcon outfit." Because ever since she let him borrow it that first time to rescue Idunn, he can't wait to wear it again, and he's basically always looking for a new excuse to dress up as a falcon every fucking chance he gets. But poor Thor doesn't know this and just goes along with it since he pretty much trusts Loki right up till the moment Loki betrays the entire fucking team later on.

But anyway, Freyja's just like, "Yeah, sure, you can borrow my falcon outfit again." So Loki thinks this is wicked pisser, and he puts the thing on, and then he flies off to fucking Giant Land and goes to this guy Thrym's house and takes the costume off and asks Thrym if he knows where Thor's hammer is. And I suppose I don't even need to say but, of course, Loki just happened to know which giant might have taken the thing since he's such a fucking weasel.

But Thrym's a vulgar douchebag, and so he's just like, "Yeah, I got Thor's fucking hammer, and I buried the damn thing eight

---

102   The other source of this particular myth, *Þrymskviða* from *The Poetic Edda*, likewise omits any explanation as to how or why the hammer suddenly disappeared from under Thor's watchful eye.

miles below ground, and there's no way anyone's ever going to see it again unless I get to marry Freyja since she's fucking gorgeous, and I'd like to tap that ass."

So Loki's just like, "Okay…" and he flies back to Asgard to tell the rest of the gods the news, and, of course, Freyja flips the fuck out and accidentally breaks the damn necklace that she got as payment for sleeping with dwarves in her rage, and, you know, it actually kind of makes me wonder if Thrym had offered her a nice necklace as part of the marriage proposal as opposed to Thor's hammer, maybe she would have gone for it, but who knows? And besides, then we wouldn't have this fun story about Thor dressing up like a chick if that'd been how it all went down.

Which is what ends up happening next since Freyja's refusing the deal, and no one can make her marry that giant asshole. So, at this point, Heimdall pipes up and is like, "Hey, why don't we just disguise Thor as a bride instead?" And all the gods think this is a no-brainer solution to their particular problem right now although Thor's not too crazy about the idea as he doesn't want to dress up in women's clothes,[103] but in the end he'll do anything to get his hammer back since he really does love that hammer, and also it's one of Asgard's primary defenses against attack so all the gods are relying on him to re-acquire it.

So they get Thor all dolled up, and then they dress Loki up as his maidservant, and together these two numbskulls[104] go get

---

[103] Prejudices were highly prevalent in the medieval manuscripts of the Norse myths, and in the *Þrymskviða* it is made clear that Thor is initially quite afraid that his peers will all henceforth mock him as a "cock craver" if he wears women's clothing and goes to a wedding dressed as the bride.

[104] It is clear throughout all of the sources of Norse mythology that Thor, despite being the strongest and one of the favorites of the gods, lacks the ability to alter the mass of his constituent god particles, unlike Odin and Loki. Why Loki chooses to dress in women's clothing himself on this occasion, rather than alter his constituent god particles or even use his full-range transmogrifier

in Thor's goat-mobile and head over Bifrost and past Heimdall's house which is right beside it. And when he comes out to see them off, he gives them both a real loud cat call, and Thor would have made a sudden u-turn and gone fucking ape-shit berserk right then and there if he was driving, but Loki's got the reins this time since the bride ain't supposed to drive herself to her own wedding, and so they just keep on going, and pretty soon they get to Thrym's house. And Thrym's gotten the place all ready for the fucking festivities since even the giants know how to have a good time, and so there's snacks and music and drinking games and whatnot. And then it's time for the main meal, and Thor just fucking gorges himself on an entire fucking ox, and eight whole salmon, and knocks back like three huge horns of mead in the first few minutes.

So Thrym sees this, and he's like, "Shit, Freyja, you can really fucking eat and drink!"

And Thor and Loki both know that Thor can't respond to that on account of his deep, booming man voice, so Loki forces out a high pitch squeak and says, "Oh yeah, that's because she's not eaten anything for the last eight days since she was so excited to get here and marry your dumb ass."

And Thrym pretty much buys this since he's a fucking idiot, and actually he thinks it's awesome that his wife-to-be can hold her own like a man when it comes to alcohol and food consumption which makes him kind of horny, and so he gets up and goes over to give Thor a kiss, and, in doing so, he lifts up the veil covering Thor's face, and he somehow misses the burly red beard[105] under there, but when he sees Thor's eyes, he gets kind of freaked out and is like, "Holy shit, Freyja, why are your eyes so fucking mean looking?! They look all blood shot, too."

---

to transform himself into an actual woman, is never explained in any of the sources.

[105]   There is no surviving evidence in any of the sources indicating that Thor ever shaved his beard for any reason.

And so, of course, Loki answers again and is like, "Because she hasn't slept for eight days since she was so excited to get here and marry you, you fucking idiot."

And I guess Thrym buys that, too. Like I said, he's pretty fucking stupid.

Amulet found in Sweden representing Thor's hammer, which he lost and then pretended to be a woman and marry an evil giant in order to recover. Wear it for protection against trolls, giants, man-eating serpents, and roving bachelor/ette parties.

So next, Thrym's nasty ass sister comes in begging for a dowry present from Thor and Loki, but they just ignore her, and then Thrym decides that going and getting Thor's hammer at this time would be a good way to get everyone's attention off his loser sister since now she's causing a scene with the photographer over by the wedding cake, and so he sends someone off to get it, and when it's brought back, they put it on Thor's lap since it's supposed to be Freyja's bridal gift and all. And so Thor happily grabs the thing, and then he throws off his wedding gown, and he just goes completely fucking nuts and kills everyone in the house except for himself and Loki, and it was fucking awesome.

Odin Experiments with
Public Vagrancy*

So one of Odin's most favorite hobbies is disguising himself as a nameless wanderer and roaming around all over Middle-Earth. Although he does stand out quite a fucking lot since he usually dresses up in some gray robes and a full-brimmed fucking hat and takes a walking stick with him, so he's not exactly inconspicuous. But anyway, one day he gets his outfit on, and he leaves his house and he decides to take the fucking train into town. So now he's wandering around the Common and the Public Gardens,[106] and he's watching the fucking swan boats glide around and taking quick nips out of the bottle that he's got hidden down in his brown paper bag under his robes, and so, of course, everyone's giving him real strange looks because they're like, "Who's that fucking freak?"[107]

---

[106]   Boston Common and Boston Public Gardens are two adjacent green spaces found in downtown Boston. Both are popular on nice days among citizens of all ages.

[107]   While the general theme of Odin traveling alone (either in disguise or under an unknown or false alias) among the world of men on Middle-Earth is commonly found throughout the Eddas and many other medieval Norse sources, his obsessive harboring of a secret bottle of booze and alcoholic tendencies are very specific details that receive an unparalleled level of attention in *The Impudent Edda*.

---

*   *This myth is the sixth of nine found in* The Impudent Edda
     *that is not attested to in either of the Elder Eddas
     or other medieval source material.*

And you know Odin, he's an old man. Oldest man out there that there is, actually, and he feels like a fucking mortal human when he goes out on his bizarre, little sojourns like this, and so in his old age, he's getting wicked tired from all this roaming around, and so he finds a nice park bench there in the shade, and he lays down on it and fucking nods off for a while till some cop eventually comes along and wakes him up and makes him move on, since, you know, he's creeping everyone else out since drunk bums aren't supposed to pass out on the benches right next to the playground where all the little kids are playing, especially if they have a history of being sex offenders like Odin does.

So then he decides, "Hey, you know, why not go for a fucking stroll down Newbury Street?"[108] Weather's never been nicer, and the cop didn't search him and find his bottle, so he continues onwards, and now he's passing all the upscale shops and restaurants and shit, and he's starting to stumble since he's gotten pretty far into his bottle by this point, but he keeps going since he's on one of his wandering missions, and Odin's not the type of guy to give up so easy, unless it's to commit suicide. And so even though he stops off a few times to rest on some of the stoops at some of the finer restaurants, he eventually makes it down to the end of the street, but then when he goes to take another swig of his barely concealed firewater, he finds out that it's completely fucking empty!

So shit, now Odin's, like, real fucking sad. He can't wander aimlessly if he's not got a beverage to help keep him company. So he gets this idea to go around the corner over to McGreevey's[109] and see if he can't order a few shots in there. So in he goes and, of course, he's looking like a complete fucking weirdo and whatnot, but the bar-

---

[108]   Newbury Street is among Boston's most fashionable shopping streets. Located in the Back Bay neighborhood, it connects directly to Boston Public Garden.

[109]   A former Irish pub in the Back Bay neighborhood, McGreevey's was co-owned by Ken Casey of the local band, The Dropkick Murphy's. As with The Asgard, McGreevey's closed during the 2020 pandemic and never reopened.

A typical park bench on Boston Common, where it is said that Odin once passed out drunk while traveling Middle-Earth.

tender's like, "Well, you know, the guy's paying cash," so at first he serves him, and everything's all right till the creepy, old geezer starts trying to hit on some of the much younger ladies sitting by him.

And well, Odin's a real vulgar motherfucker so this isn't just your usual harmless old guy commentary, but he's making some real strong passes at them with thinly veiled references to his wiener, and it's just getting ugly, and the bartender's realizing this crazy, old bastard's causing trouble so he asks him to settle up and leave, and Odin refuses and the situation goes south real fucking fast, and next thing you know, he's being escorted out the door and tossed out onto the fucking pavement.[110]

---

110   Other instances of Odin's solo travels on Middle-Earth frequently feature the successful seduction of young, vulnerable women, as opposed to a failed effort that leaves him quite liter-

McGreevey's on Boylston Street in Boston's Back Bay. Owned by Ken Casey of The Dropkick Murphys, the now-defunct bar is most assuredly only one of many in the greater Boston area to have forcibly removed Odin from the premises for illicit and foul-tempered drunken behavior.

So he gets up, spews his guts out all over the hood of the nearest parked car, and then he continues to stumble across the street,

---

ally out in the cold as occurs here. One of the most significant examples of this occurs in the *Hárbarðsljóð* of *The Poetic Edda*, in which Odin, disguised as the cantankerous, old ferry man Harbard, gets into a pissing contest with Thor, who wishes to employ the ferryman's services but fails to recognize that the ferryman is, in fact, his father, Odin, who is just giving him a hard time. During the course of their clash of egos, Harbard brags about his sexual prowess, specifically regarding the time that he slept with seven sisters when he was out traveling and causing mayhem in Middle-Earth on the island of Algron. More recently, Odin's seduction abilities—again, specifically in the guise of Harbard—have been featured on the History Channel's full-blown anti-history television series, *Vikings*.

thinking, you know, maybe he'll just go into the library where it's all nice and warm and find a cozy little corner somewhere where he can pass out amongst the books since he fucking loves sleeping surrounded by books since he loves the knowledge they contain, but it's fucking super late at night now, and the doors are all locked, and so he sits down on the steps in front of the fucking place and passes out till morning like a fucking loser.

Sad, Flaccid Sex God

All right, so one day Frey decides to go and sit up in Odin's chair[111] when the old fart wasn't around, which, you know, you aren't supposed to do, but he went and did it anyway since, you know, he's a fucking god himself, and he figures he can get away with it. Now the thing with Odin's chair is it's magical just like every other fucking object in Asgard, and the point being that if you sit in Odin's chair, then you get to see everything else that's happening across the whole wide world.[112]

Now the thing about Frey is, he's basically got a permanent boner,[113] so you can just imagine how he jumps at the chance to

---

111   The Elder Eddas both identify Odin's special throne with the suitably epic-sounding name of Hlidskjalf.

112   While the exact machinations of Odin's chair remain unknown, it has been suggested that Hlidskjalf is equiped with an early model flux capacitor that, when engaged, enables the user to manipulate and bend the curvature of the space-time continuum, and thereby pass between select but disparate space-time intervals along the great ash-like, high-energy intersteller structure known as Yggdrasil. The fragility of early Norse flux capacitor technology, along with its potential to induce tree blight upon Yggdrasil's branches when improperly used, makes a strong case for Odin's forbiddance of anyone who lacks the proper training from sitting in his chair.

113   As a fertility god, Frey is well-endowed beyond all plausibility and was, consequently, highly renowned for his phallic asset among the ancient Scandinavians, as attested by the numerous Viking Age depictions of his gargantuan dong.

go full-out peeping Tom-style on all the pretty ladies while they're in the shower. So he's sitting there in Odin's chair, and he's going from house to house spying on all the naked girls[114] like some sort of loser teenager from an 80s movie when he just so happens to come across the hottest giantess[115] this side of a Vegas showgirls extravaganza, and him being the horny dog that he is, well, he decides that he's not going to be able to go on living if he's not able to fuck this chick.

Now him being a sex god and all, you'd think he could probably figure out a way to hook this up for himself, but somehow he instead gets completely fucking depressed, and then he goes home and he locks himself up in his own house like a fucking jackass, and now he won't even talk to anybody.

So his dad, Njord, finally gets wind of this, and he's like, "Ah great, here we go again." And so instead of dealing with it himself like he normally does since he's just not in the mood, he instead decides to send Skirnir over to Frey's house to check up on him since Skirnir's kind of the gods' bitch.

Anyway, so Skirnir goes over to Frey's house, and when Frey answers the door, he's fucking crying and he's like, "Skirnir, you got to help me, man, I've lost my boner!" And so of course Skirnir's just like, "What the fuck?" and ends up having to babysit Frey's dumb ass till he calms his liver, and then he ends up finding out that Frey's convinced his dick is never going to get hard

---

114   This is a new and important detail unique to *The Impudent Edda*. The Elder Eddas and other older sources do not indicate that Frey's sole objective of sitting in Hlidskjalf was to spy on nude women.

115   Both the *Gylfaginning* from *The Prose Edda* and the *För Skírnis* poem from *The Poetic Edda* identify this voluptuous giantess as Gerd, the daughter of the giant, Gymir, and his wife, Aurboda. Additionally, the *Skáldskaparmál* from *The Prose Edda* and the *Lokasenna* from *The Poetic Edda* both seem to indicate that Gymir is another name for Aegir, the bizarrely friendly giant and lord of the sea.

Perhaps the most famous depiction of Frey's monstrous manhood is this 11th century figurine from Södermanland, Sweden, in which he is sitting in a cross-legged position with his boner upright and on prominent display.

again unless he can bang that hot giantess he spied on when he shouldn't have even been looking in the first place. And since Skirnir's kind of a bitch, he goes and he ends up making a promise to Frey that he'll go and look for this girl and propose to her for him on his behalf. But also, he makes sure he's not going to come out of this deal empty-handed himself, so he bargains for Frey's horse and his magic sword, and Frey agrees, which was a pretty dumb fucking move on his part. Because no matter how hot this girl might have been, she's still a fucking two-faced giantess, but his sword, in particular on the other hand, is part of what makes him such a fucking legend.[116]

---

[116]   Frey's sword is reputed to be imbued with unique isotopic properties that allow it to fight entirely on its own accord. Unfor-

So anyway, Skirnir goes off and he convinces this giantess to marry that crazy bastard, and Skirnir ends up getting the magic sword when all's said and done, and Frey gets his boner back. So good for them both, I guess.[117]

---

tunately, little more is known about this sword. It has not received the same degree of scientific study as have certain other highly technical ancient Scandinavian devices, such as Freyja's falcon transmogrifier or Odin's flux capacitor chair.

[117]   *The Impudent Edda*, much like *The Prose Edda*, offers only a very abbreviated version of this particular myth. *The Poetic Edda*'s *För Skírnis*, however, delves into much deeper detail in its description of Skirnir's journey. In that rendition of the myth, Skirnir rides through a wall of flames and past an unfriendly herdsman en route to Gerd's hall in Giant Land, whereupon he offers her a selection of Idunn's apples of youth and Odin's special ring, Draupnir, in exchange for her hand in marriage to Frey (how Skirnir came to possess these items remains a mystery). Gerd refuses this generous offer because she cannot envision herself happily marrying her brother's murderer (in *The Prose Edda*'s *Gylfaginning*, Snorri relates that Frey slew Gerd's brother, Beli, with a deer's antlers for reasons unknown). Skirnir then threatens to decapitate her with Frey's sword if she does not agree to the marriage, but even with that death threat, Gerd refuses, at which point Skirnir unleashes a curse through the carving of runes upon her soul that would make even grim, old Odin blush. Skirnir condemns Gerd to an eternity of misery characterized by extreme isolation, physical disfiguration, a lifelong diet of nothing but goat urine, and an insatiable craving for sex with her only potential accommodaters being hideous trolls. When he finally finishes unleashing this torrent of torment, Gerd backs down and agrees to marry Frey nine days thence in the woods of Barri. Conversely, in the *Heimskringla*'s *Ynglinga Saga*, Frey and Gerd become mortals and play the role of the progenitors to the royal line of ancient Swedish kings.

Thor Renews His Driver's License*

Oh god, so poor fucking Thor, man! He has to go get his driver's license renewed since it's about to expire, and he has to get his photo taken, too, since the last time he did that was more than nine years ago, and they don't let you do it online when it's been that long. Which would suck for anyone, but I really don't get it in Thor's case. I mean, the guy doesn't even age; he fucking popped out of his mother's womb[118] looking like a full-grown body builder with a prickly red beard, and he's going to stay looking that way till the end of time when the fucking serpent poisons him to death. But I guess not even a divine entity like Thor can escape the long arm of the RMV.[119]

---

[118]   Thor's mother is the Earth, so his birth most likely involved catastrophic geotechtonic plate movement at the Earth's surface as his mother violently convulsed and pushed him upward from her deep, plasmic core through her cavernous, igneous birth canal and into the bright light of day.

[119]   Unlike the vast majority of the U.S., Massachussets does not use the more commonly found moniker of DMV for its state agency responsible for motor vehicle regulation. Instead, it uses RMV, which stands for Registry of Motor Vehicles. Also, worthy of note is that it is perhaps no coincidence that driver's license photos were valid for a period of nine years in Massachusetts at the time

*   *This myth is the seventh of nine found in* The Impudent Edda *that is not attested to in either of the Elder Eddas or other medieval source material.*

And as you'd fucking know it, Thor's been out all night drinking the night before, and so he sleeps through his fucking alarm clock and doesn't get his ass down to Haymarket[120] till fucking like half past nine. Now there's these couple of birds sitting on a telephone wire shit-talking each other, and when they see Thor coming they're fucking like, "Look at that dipshit driving a couple of goats! What a fucking moron! He's never going to find a place to park at this time. What the fuck's he thinking?" But Thor's got no idea what they're saying since he's never eaten a dragon's heart[121] before, and so he's figuring he's going to be able

---

of *The Impudent Edda*'s recording, since nine has also always been an important number in Norse mythology.

[120]   The iconic location of a historic outdoor market in downtown Boston.

[121]   This is an indirect reference to one of the most famous sagas of the ancient Scandinavians and Germans: that of Sigurd the Dragon-Slayer. The story has been recorded in numerous manuscripts and formats over the years, having been preserved not only as a stand-alone saga of its own in *Völsunga Saga* but also in the heroic (not mythological) poems of *The Poetic Edda* and in an abbreviated format in the *Skáldskaparmál* of *The Prose Edda*. While Sigurd's story does not figure directly into *The Impudent Edda*, the pertinent part that is referenced here about the consumption of a dragon's heart comprises one of its most famous scenes. In that particular scene, Sigurd has just slain the dragon, Fafnir, and is seated beside a campfire with Regin, Fafnir's brother (Fafnir had once been human but used an ancient transmogrifier to shape-shift into dragon form earlier in the saga). Fafnir's heart is presently roasting over the fire, and when Sigurd tastes its juices to determine whether it is fully cooked, he suddenly gains the ability to understand the avian language. Sitting in a tree above him are two birds who at that precise moment just so happen to be discussing with certainty the notion that Regin will soon attempt to slay Sigurd. Having heard this, Sigurd preemptively strikes and kills Regin first, while he sleeps. Thor, on the other hand, has never actually tasted the sweet nectar of roast dragon's heart, and thus cannot comprehend what the birds above him are saying at Haymarket.

Brick and concrete parking garage in downtown Boston
where it is said that Thor once parked his goats for an entire
day while he dealt with getting his driver's license renewed.

to find a place to park, but, naturally, the birds are right and all
the on-street parking spots are already long gone, and so now he's
driving his goats around and around in fucking circles downtown,
flipping off every jackass who cuts him off till finally he just gives
the fuck up and goes and parks in the fucking garage.

So now he locks the goats up, and he goes into the RMV and
takes a number, and he sits down and proceeds to start waiting. So
he's sitting there now, looking around the room at this god-hon-
est public display of human fucking misery, and even though no
one's talking to each other, you could just cut the tension in that
room with a fucking spoon. But you know, Thor's an energetic,
sociable guy, and, eventually, he just can't help keeping quiet anymore, and so he starts telling the little, old Caribbean lady sitting
beside him about the time that he decapitated some trolls and

then went bowling with their heads with Loki afterwards, but she just gives him a weird look and gets up and goes and sits down on the other side of the room since no one wants to sit next to a fucking freak at the RMV.

So now it's like mid-afternoon, and they finally call Thor's number, and so he gets up and he goes over to the counter that's got his number flashing above it, and he just about spazzes the fuck out when the lifeless zombie creature[122] on the other side of the glass starts talking to him like a genuine troll. I mean, for a guy who makes a living killing monsters, it's kind of like a fucking miracle that he didn't just react on reflex and murder this cretin right there on the fucking spot. They don't always employ humans in these places, you know?

But anyway, Thor fills out his paperwork, and he gets his picture taken, and so then he finally leaves that hellhole, but by now it's fucking rush hour, and so he's forced to pay an arm and a leg for his fucking parking spot, and then he starts up his goats, pulls out of the garage, and proceeds to spend the rest of the night in stop-and-go traffic, watching each of his goats drop a deuce every time he applies some pressure on the fucking brakes.

It was a super shitty day.

---

122 Such nightmarish zombie creatures are usually referred to as "draugr" in the old Icelandic sources. A particularly famous one is featured in *Grettis saga Ásmundarsonar* in which the saga's namesake protagonist, Grettir, battles and slays the draugr known as Glam, but not before Glam curses him, his undead and gleaming, evil yellow eyes haunting Grettir in the dark to the very end of his days.

Hostile Cattle Decapitation Day

So can you believe this shit? All the gods are over at Thor's house partying hard since that's what they do, and they run out of fucking booze!

Which is just fucking stupid. I don't know which of those dick-heads showed up empty-handed or not, but it doesn't really matter because then they get this wicked pisser idea that they'll just go and crash Aegir's place since he lives at the bottom of the ocean, and he's surrounded by all that seawater so he always has some new batch of beer brewing.

So the gods go and they show up at Aegir's underwater house, and he's like, "Oh fuck, I only ever brew small batches of craft beer. I ain't got enough on hand for all of you, and I don't even got the right size of cauldron to brew as much as we'd need for all of us to get properly shit-faced tonight, either."

Then at this point, Tyr is like, "Hey guys, my dad, the evil frost giant Hymir, has a big-ass cauldron. It's like fucking five miles deep."

And Odin likes the sounds of this, so he commands Tyr to go steal it from his dad, but Tyr is like, "Well, I can't go get the damn thing and carry it back all by myself since I only got one hand since you assholes all made me get my other one bitten off by that fucking wolf."

So Thor volunteers to help since he likes traveling into enemy territory, and he figures, you know, maybe he'll get a chance to kill some hostile giants on the way, which is his top priority in life besides drinking and making thunder, so for him it's like

a win-win, you know? So he and Tyr take off and they get to
Tyr's parents' house and go inside, and his parents aren't there
but his senile old grandma who has nine-hundred fucking heads
is but they just ignore her because, fuck, how the fuck are you
supposed to hold a meaningful conversation with nine-hundred
heads' worth of supernatural dementia?

Anyway, eventually, Tyr's mom comes home and she sees her
little boy's lost one of his hands, and so she starts fretting all over
about this and reprimanding him for not being more careful when
he plays with talking wolves and shit till finally they hear his dad
pull up into the driveway, and then she's like, "Fuck! You guys
better hide! He's been in an extra shitty mood all fucking day!"

So Tyr and Thor run and hide under one of Hymir's many gi-
ant-ass cauldrons while they listen to Tyr's mom tell his dad that
their boy's back in town and that he's got a guest with him. Well,
this sends Hymir into a fucking rage since he has a conflicted
relationship with his son, and so he starts tearing the rafters off
the ceiling and knocking the cauldrons over and shit, but then
he calms down and realizes that, you know, maybe he ought to
try and be nice to his kid before going fucking bonkers like that.
So then at this point, Tyr and Thor come out of hiding, and they
all decide to have dinner together so the hosts start preparing a
meal, and then eventually they all sit down to eat.

Now Thor, he's not always the most gracious of guests. That's
one of his character flaws, unfortunately, since he's pretty fucking awesome in most other ways. But anyway, so out of the
three oxes prepared for this meal, Thor downs two of them all
by himself before the others even finish their first bite. And, of
course, this rubs Hymir the wrong way, but he just chokes his
anger down and says that if they want to finish the meal, then he
and Thor better go fishing to get more food. So they're getting
the boat ready, and Thor's kind of awkward at it since he doesn't
go fishing all that often, and Hymir just starts letting him have
it with all these little, under-handed comments about Thor's
fishing abilities. Basically, he tells Thor that he's a little bitch.

And as I'm sure you already realize at this point, Thor's got a fucking temper, and no one calls him a little bitch and gets away with it. But at this particular moment, he somehow managed to swallow his pride so that instead of whipping out his special hammer and fucking flat-out killing the jackass right there on the fucking spot like he usually does, he just challenged him instead. He was like, "Hey Hymir, fuck you. And while we're at it, I bet I can row out to sea farther than you can. Oh, and by the way, I bet your dick's smaller than a dwarf's."[123]

And then to really get at him, Thor went out into the woods right after he said that to where all Hymir's oxes were, and he found the biggest, baddest, most powerful and prized of all the oxes,[124] and then he just proceeded to fucking rip its head off with his bare fucking hands.

So now Thor's walking back to Hymir's house, carrying this dead ox head, you know, fucking dripping blood all over the fucking place since he didn't have the patience to let the thing dry out since this is Thor we're talking about, and Thor is not a patient individual, and the whole time he's fantasizing about all the different ways he can use this decapitated ox head to get back at Hymir, and the whole thing's making him happier than an alcoholic leprechuan guzzling Guinness straight out of a bottomless pot of gold on Saint Patty's Day.

But in the meantime, Hymir's inner rage's been boiling on account of the fact that Thor just told him he has a wicked tiny dick. I mean, he's a fucking giant, right? Nobody gets away with telling a giant he's got a little dick unless it's Thor. I'm not even sure if Odin could get away with pulling that one off since, you know,

---

[123] While instances of penis size-related insults and humilation are not entirely uncommon to the Old Norse literary material, the prior versions of this myth do not include the exchange of foul-mouthed, dick-related insults. This is a new and insightful embellishment provided by *The Impudent Edda*.

[124] In *The Prose Edda*'s *Gylfaginning*, Snorri relates that this special ox is named Himinhrjot.

he's not as strong as Thor is, but then he's also a lot more wiser so he pry wouldn't have insulted the guy like that in the first place.

But anyway, so now Thor comes back with Hymir's decapitated ox head, and he hides the thing right there in Hymir's boat so that Hymir can't see it, and then they row off to go fishing together because Hymir's decided to take Thor up on his challenge about who can row the farthest.

But so now they're out there on the open water, and Hymir's like, "Hey, let's fish here." And Thor's like, "Shut the fuck up, we're not stopping till we get past the Outer Banks!"

But Hymir doesn't want to keep going, so he's like, "But come on, Thor, what's wrong with where we're at right now? Look at all the fucking fish. There's a lot of fucking fish here."

And Thor nearly fucking loses it! He's like, "You shut the fuck up right now, you fucking piece of shit! I am not going to be shown up by some fucking Brahmin rat bastard from fucking Hollywood!"

And then Thor just mumbles something about how George Clooney can go and fuck himself, and Hymir kind of doesn't get what all Thor's talking about since he's never seen *The Perfect Storm*, but he backs down anyway, and then they keep on rowing out there fucking farther and farther and farther out into the water.[125]

So they're getting pretty far out there now, and it's starting to make Hymir real uneasy because now they're starting to get real close to the Middle-Earth Serpent's home waters, and even though Hymir's a prick giant himself, giants don't always get along with that fucking snake any better than the gods do, at least not till they decide to team up with it in order to murder all the gods and destroy the entire fucking universe by setting it on fire one day. So he's like, "Hey, man, aren't we far enough out to sea by now?"

---

[125]   In another recent development, the lore and historic tragedies of the fishermen of maritime Gloucester, Massachusetts appear to have infiltrated and influenced the myth at this point in *The Impudent Edda*'s telling.

But do you think Thor gives a shit?

THOR DOES NOT GIVE A SHIT!!!

This is exactly what Thor wants! And so now Hymir's basically shitting his pants, and he fucking drops his oar, and so now Thor has to keep on rowing the boat all by himself, and he's getting really worked up and so he's calling in the storm clouds to make some fucking thunder, and he keeps going like this till finally they're at the edge of the ocean and floating right over the fucking serpent itself.

Now at this point, Thor gets out the decapitated ox head, and he starts to tie it to a fishing line, and, normally, this would have caused Hymir to get right up in his face as soon as he saw this because he recognizes it as his own best ox, and he didn't know Thor had gone and ripped off its fucking head with his bare fucking hands, but he's so scared shitless at this point on account of the fact that the fucking serpent's lurking there in the water right beneath them.

So now it's lightning like crazy in the sky above since that's what Thor wants, and so he casts this line out with the decapitated ox head on it as bait, and as soon as it sinks down he gets a bite, and he starts reeling it in like a fucking maniac, and his feet break through the hull of the boat, and so now he's standing there on the bottom of the seabed, and then before you even fucking know it, the serpent's breaking through the waves all around the boat, and this thing is mean, and I mean, real fucking mean. He's a vicious fucking sea snake fucking monstrosity, and he's spitting poison all over the place, and he's snarling like a fucking demon straight out of hell, and he's got the fishing line hook caught in his mouth, and so he can't get away, and it's making him angry, and so him and Thor are just staring at each other straight in the fucking eyes with the lightning flashing all around them, and Thor's standing there holding the fishing rod with one hand, and he's reaching for his magic hammer with the other so that he can use it to fucking pound the living shit out of this goddamn piece of shit snake for once and for all, when all of a sudden that shit-for-brains giant, Hymir, goes and cuts the fucking line!

Bronze dragon-head from Denmark. It represents exactly the sort of nefarious sea creature you don't ever want to see while fishing, unless you are a hot-headed, monster-killing machine like Thor.

He's such a fucking worthless piece of shit! I swear to god, never go fishing with a giant. Ever. They're all fucking worthless useless assholes that make the Kardashians look like productive members of society.

But now because of this, the serpent sinks back into the water, but Thor at least reacts real fucking fast because he throws Mjölnir into the water after it, but I guess magical hammers just aren't made like they used to be because the fucking serpent survives, but Thor at least gets his hammer back since it works kind of like a boomerang.[126]

---

[126]   Thor's hammer, Mjölnir, was forged with the specific purpose of functioning as a unique airfoil that returns to Thor each

But he's so fucking pissed. I mean, you would not even want to be anywhere near him right now, he's so fucking pissed, and so he just punches that asshole, Hymir, right in the fucking face, and Hymir falls overboard, and Thor just leaves him there to drown out in the middle of the fucking ocean, which is pretty much what he deserves, the fucking loser. And then Thor rows on back to shore, and he and Tyr steal the cauldron while Tyr's mom goes and deals with trying to prevent Hymir from drowning to death.[127]

---

and every time that he hurls it. Thanks to its utilization of the mechanical physics of aerodynamic uplift in the near-space atmospheric conditions that exist in both Middle-Earth and Giant Land (where most of Thor's hammer-throwing campaigns occur), Mjölnir flies along a parabolic trajectory as determined by the mass and acceleration of Thor's muscular throwing arm. The resultant angular spin velocity applies a torque to Mjölnir, creating a gyroscopic precession that leads it directly back to Thor's outstretched hand.

[127]   Thor's fishing trip with Hymir and their shipboard confrontation with the Middle-Earth Serpent has always been one of the most popular of the Norse myths, and consequently, multiple variations regarding the specifics of the events detailed within it have been passed down through the ages. In addition to its inclusion, albeit with substantially different plotlines, in both *The Poetic Edda* and *The Prose Edda*, remnants of this particular myth have also survived in multiple skaldic poems dating from the medieval time period. These sources all vary in terms of the content of the myth, particularly concerning the gods' reasons for visiting Hymir in the first place, and the aftermath of the fishing trip. *The Impudent Edda*'s version appears to be a hybrid of the two Elder Eddas, with new details added.

The segment leading up to the actual fishing trip most closely resembles that found in *The Poetic Edda*'s *Hymiskviða*, in which the gods' desperate need to brew more beer drives Thor and Tyr off in search of Hymir's cauldron. However, while rowing en route to the serpent's home waters, the *Hymiskviða* relates that Hymir catches two whales, which is corroborated in neither *The Prose*

And then when Tyr and Thor finally get back to Aegir's place, Aegir starts brewing a shit-ton of beer, and they all get shit-faced and pass out there at his house under the water.

---

nor *Impudent Edda*s. Furthermore, the aftermath of the fishing trip in the *Hymiskviða* version involves the return of both Hymir and Thor to Hymir's hall, where Hymir begrudgingly relinquishes his cauldron, challenges Thor to break a deceptively strong goblet, and then chases after Thor and Tyr with a horde of giants as they lug the cauldron away, whereupon Thor goes berserk and kills every last one of them in an insane but joyous giant-slaying rampage. Snorri's version in the *Gylfaginning* of *The Prose Edda*, on the other hand, presents Thor as a solo traveler who goes to Hymir's hall in the guise of a young boy for the sole purpose of wrecking carnage (though whether his initial intentions are to kill giants or battle the serpent remain unclear). Snorri's version is also the first to reveal that Hymir cuts the fishing line to release the serpent and that Thor throws Mjölnir after it. This version does not involve a cauldron at any point in the story, and simply ends with Thor punching Hymir in the face, knocking him overboard.

Lastly, it should be noted that some scholars have suggested that Tyr is actually Loki in this myth, and that the role was conflated early on and perpetuated ever since. Loki, taking the part of Tyr, would be more consistent with other stories found throughout Norse mythology, across all sources, both in terms of his parentage (giants) and his role as Thor's usual traveling companion. Additonally, the word "Tyr" may originate as a much more general term for "god" that could apply to all the gods in a general sense, not just the one-handed deity in question. Nevertheless, *The Impudent Edda* continues the tradition of the more common version of this myth in which Tyr plays the part rather than Loki.

Asgard Hosts a Pumpkin Festival*

So now Odin's at home in Valaskjalf[128] sitting on his special magical shitter called Shit Throne,[129] and I can't remember what it's called in Old fucking Norse, but it's something fucking epic that literally means Shit Throne, and it has special magical self-cleansing properties and, of course, a fucking bidet, too, since you know how Odin is. Anyway, he can't just simply take a dump without learning some new wisdom and shit, so he's reading his favorite bathroom copy of *The Guinness Book of World Records*, and he gets to the part about the world record for the most lit jack-o-lanterns, and he just about loses his shit. I mean, he's sitting there, reading this, and going, "You got to be fucking shitting me! Some tiny ass town in the middle of nowhere in Middle-Earth has the world fucking record for the most lit jack-o-lanterns at any one time?! That's fucking bullshit!!!"[130] And so he resolved himself right then

---

[128] Valaskjalf is one of Odin's halls in Asgard; Valaskjalf is where he keeps Hlidskjalf, his magic chair.

[129] This is the first-ever documented mention of Shit Throne. Precious little is known about it, but it in all likelihood it is equipped with ancient Scandinavian flux capacitor technology.

[130] The small town of Keene, New Hampshire presently holds the Guinness World Record for most lit jack-o-lanterns with a staggering total of 30,581.

---

* *This myth is the eighth of nine found in* The Impudent Edda *that is not attested to in either of the Elder Eddas or other medieval source material.*

and there that Asgard is going to set a new record, and as soon as he's done with his business on Shit Throne, he sets about planning the biggest fucking pumpkin festival of all fucking time.

And there's a ton of logistical planning that goes into planning a pumpkin festival, you know? Plus on top of that, Asgard isn't exactly known for having all sorts of pumpkin patches planted all over the fucking place. So this ends up being another one of those instances where Odin sends Skirnir off to do his bitch work, and Skirnir seems okay with it since he managed to extort a lifetime supply of pumpkin spice lattes out of Odin in exchange for going over to Middle-Earth and collecting all the goddamn pumpkins growing over here.

So while Skirnir's off collecting gourds and shit, Odin's busy sending invitations and trying to convince everyone else in Asgard to participate in his fucking pumpkin festival. And both Thor and Loki get pretty excited about it as soon as they hear about it, so they agree right away and begin building various wooden frameworks to display the pumpkins on, and Frigg and Idunn team up to start brewing a massive amount of hot apple cider, and Frey decides to go and set up a fucking huge ass corn maze.

But Freyja's nowhere to be seen, and this has do with the fact that when Odin sent her an invitation, he also included another goddamned dick pic with it. So she texted him to fuck off and then turned off her phone. And even though she keeps changing her number, it never does any good since Odin's the fucking All Father, and he's in charge of the 9 Worlds' mobile network, so everytime she changes numbers, he just gets a notification and starts texting her dick pics at her new one. But, you know, even though she's a divine sex goddess, she's still just as addicted to her fucking phone as the next guy, so she can't give it up completely without feeling like her heart's been cut out of her fucking chest.[131]

---

131 There exists a distinct possibility that Freyja may, in fact, actually know what it feels like to have her heart cut out of her chest, provided it's been burned first. The Eddic poem, *Hyndlul-*

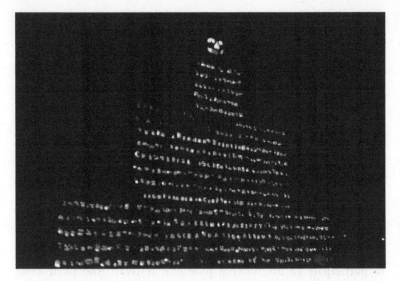

*Jack-o-lantern tower in Keene, New Hampshire, the ongoing
holder of the record for most lit jack-o-lanterns, since Odin
failed to invite a member of the Guinness World Records
organization to his superior festival.*

There's just no winning when it comes to technology depen-
dency, you know?

But, you know, after a while, it all starts to come together, and
Skirnir gets back from Middle-Earth with nine million pumpkins, and then Odin makes the Einherjar[132] stop killing each oth-

---

jóð, mentions that Loki ate a burnt woman's heart. The textual
evidence is unclear regarding exactly whose heart this is—presumably, it belonged to Gullveig, the witch whom Odin murdered in the myth, *How Not to Get Away with Witch Murder.* But
if Gullveig was, in fact, Freyja (see footnote 21), then this would
have been Freyja's heart. Alternatively, it might have belonged to
Angrboda (the ogress mother of Loki's monstrous children). In
any event, Freyja does not wish to ever give up her phone.

132   The Einherjar are Odin's dead warriors who inhabit Valhalla, where they fight and feast every day.

er and start carving the pumpkins instead. And they weren't at all pleased about this, but Odin threatened to withhold goat-mead from them, so they took their swords and knives and axes and began carving all sorts of wicked cool jack-o-lanterns, and as soon as each jack-o-lantern was ready, Loki'd light the candle inside it on fire with his fucking mind, and then Thor would find a place for it to go in the vast assortment of frameworks they'd built to display these things on.

And then pretty soon it was time for the big day!

And, of course, it was fall in Asgard and the weather was just perfect. Cool and crisp in the air, you know? And Yggdrasil's leaves were bright orange and yellow and red and blue and magenta and silver. And all the gods and goddesses came. Even Heimdall took a break from guarding the stupid, fucking bridge to come enjoy Odin's nine million glowing jack-o-lanterns and Frigg's and Idunn's special spiced alcoholic apple cider. And all the elves and dwarves and various land and water spirits came out, too. But Odin didn't invite the giants since they're a bunch of dicks, so there were no giants in attendence.

And Freyja wasn't there, either, although she did send Odin a cart-load of jack-o-lanterns carved to look like cat's asses with the tails lifted, all of which were filled to the brim with cat shit.

But everyone who went had a great fucking time. Odin's a guy who really knows how to host a pumpkin festival. It probably helps being the top deity in all existence, but still. The only thing is he didn't invite anyone from Middle-Earth since he looks down on mortal humans. But this also meant that no one was there from the Guinness World Records organization to validate his event, so even though Odin's pumpkin festival totally blew the old record out of the water, it still didn't make it into the fucking *Guinness Book of World Records.*

Thor Wades through the
Menstrual Fluid Fjord†

Now for whatever reason, Loki's developed a real unhealthy obsession with falcon outfits,[133] and I don't know why, but that's how it is, and so he fucking goes and he steals the one that Frigg owns one day.[134] Basically, what I think happened is that Filene's

---

[133] Loki's perplexing fixation on early model, falcon-form transmogrifiers is never adequately explained in any of the Eddas. While in prior instances, he seemed most obsessed with the one that belonged to Freyja (perhaps as part of his deviant sexual obsession with her extremely alluring feminine physique that motivated his consequent criminal stalking activities as related in the myth, *The Night Freyja Walked the Streets*), here he has instead deflected his attention to the one owned by Frigg. There is no explanation that clarifies this in any of the surviving sources, but one can easily imagine a long lost myth in which Freyja tells Loki off, strictly instructing him never to inquire about her falcon outfit nor attempt to break into her house ever again.

[134] *The Impudent Edda*'s version of this myth most closely

---

† The Impudent Edda*'s erratic aside known as* The Lay of the Bs *immediately precedes this myth in the original recording of the* Codex Bostonia. *However, because it severely disrupts the mythological narrative arc while simultaneously offering very little of interest or value, it has been removed from its traditional position in this volume. A complete translation of* The Lay of the Bs *may be found in the Appendix for any serious students of Impudent Eddic knowledge who actually wish to read it anyway.*

The original site of Filene's and Filene's Basement in downtown Boston, where it is said that Freyja and Frigg purchased their stylish falcon outfits at a special, discounted price, before the retail chain was bought and shuttered by Macy's.

Basement had a major sale on these falcon outfits a while back, and so Frigg and Freyja had gone shopping together and each of

resembles that found in the *Skáldskaparmál* of *The Prose Edda*, but provides many new, hithertofore unknown details about the events described, the first of which involves Loki's means of acquiring Frigg's falcon outfit; the *Skáldskaparmál* does not relate whether it was stolen or borrowed. While this particular myth is not accounted for in *The Poetic Edda*, it does exist in a substantially differentiated form in the *Þórsdrápa*, a skaldic poem composed by Eilif Guthrunarson in the 10th century in which Thor travels with Thialfi (his servant) rather than Loki and does not leave his beloved hammer behind.

them got one. But whatever, the point is Loki steals the thing, and then he goes and he transforms himself into a fucking falcon with its magical properties, and then he flies off to Giant Land.

So now he gets up into the air, and he's passing through Middle-Earth on his way to Giant Land, and he's flying over this huge ass fucking massacre on the ground where tons of guys just fucking all-out killed each other all over the place, and so he's having to dodge the fucking valkyries at rush hour since they're liable to kill him in a violent collision, not to mention if he even survived, it'd fucking jack up his vehicular falcon outfit insurance rates, so he's taking it pretty easy till he gets clear of that mess, and then he decides to pull off at the first giant's house he sees to take a bit of a break. So he lands on the window sill of the first house he sees, and he starts staring through the window at this guy, Geirrod, who's a real raging dick-head.

So Geirrod's just sitting there, vegging out on the couch since he's just having a lazy Sunday, but then Geirrod sees Loki in falcon form and orders one of his minions to go and catch the fucking bird, but this minion is a real fucking shit-head who can barely climb, and so Loki's just sitting up there laughing his ass off because it's like watching a fucking cartoon with this moron tripping all over himself, but then he finally starts to get close, and Loki goes to fly away, and he can't because his feet are fucking stuck to the window sill! So the minion grabs him and yanks him off the window sill and then hands him off to Geirrod who looks real close at Loki and then just fucking screams in his face like a goddamned maniac since he's an evil giant, and then he locks Loki away in a fucking chest and goes and gets some chips and dip to snack on since the game's about to start.

So now Loki's locked in there, starving his ass off and going out of his fucking mind since he just got out-smarted by this asshole of a giant, and he can't get away, and the days and the weeks are starting to tick by till finally Geirrod opens the chest up again after fucking like three months and tells him that he'll let him go, but only if he promises to lure Thor back to his house without his special magical hammer, to which Loki agrees since he's a piece of shit.

So Loki heads back to Asgard and returns Frigg's falcon outfit without her noticing it was ever even missing in the first place, and then he goes to talk to Thor where he proceeds to tell him that he found this secret place full of super hot, sexy giant women who kept asking about Thor and saying how they all wanted to take turns jumping his bones, but only if he went to them unarmed since they're pacifists.[135] Which doesn't really make any sense since they're giants, and there's no such thing as a pacifist giant, but poor Thor, he's never been the brightest bulb on the block, and so he bought this hook, line, and sinker, and he forgot he even owned a fucking hammer and was on his way out the door following Loki like a homeless dog begging for attention.

So now these guys enter Giant Land, and Thor sees a souvenir shop right when they enter so he goes into it and buys a pair of gloves, a belt, and a walking stick[136] since he wants to be ready for the rough topography ahead, and he didn't really come prepared

---

135 This is another new detail provided by *The Impudent Edda*. In the *Skáldskaparmál* no reason is given as to why Thor left behind his beloved hammer, which is highly out of character for him. It is entirely plausible that he would do so if it meant getting to sleep with a bevy of beautiful giantesses, as the poet of *The Impudent Edda* suggests, but the notion that these giantesses themselves would be pacifists and offended by the presence of a medieval weapon is itself highly unlikely, just as the anonymous poet states. Whichever way this myth is meant to be interpreted, it features a break in typical Norse mythological logic.

136 This is another deviation from the more traditional version of the myth set forth by the *Skáldskaparmál*. According to Snorri, Thor and Loki do not stop at a souvenir shop but rather at the home of the oddly friendly giantess, Grid, who is also the mother of Odin's son, Vidar. Grid warns Thor while Loki is sleeping that all is not what it seems and that danger awaits him at Geirrod's hall. In Snorri's version, it is Grid who gives Thor the iron gloves, belt of strength, and staff.

at all. Then they get back on the trail, and they come to this huge fucking river that's overflowing like the worst spring thaw ever on record.

So they're just staring at this fucking flood, and then Thor is like, "All right, Loki, why don't you just grab onto my special belt that I just bought?" And Loki's like, "Yeah, I guess I will." Since Thor's kind of like a body builder and super strong, and so he just wades on out into the water like a hardcore fucking badass with Loki dangling along like the whiny, little bitch that he is.

Well, they're only fucking like halfway across the damn river when all of sudden it starts to rise even higher! So now Thor's digging his new staff into the river bed and stirring up all sorts of early 20th century contaminants that must have been buried down there since the fucking mill closed in the '60s, and he's using all of his strength just to keep from being swept away when he looks up and he sees this nasty ass giant bitch[137] standing on top of the hill upstream, squatting above the water and menstruating straight into the goddamned river itself!

So at first Thor just gags because, fuck, that's just downright unhygienic, you know? But then he gets over it, and he grabs a fucking rock and he hurls the thing straight at her face, and it clocks her right in the fucking forehead, and she goes down and the river recedes, and then he and Loki are able to finally get to the other side.[138]

So now Thor's really starting to hope that that wasn't one of the really hot giant women that Loki'd been talking about, but they keep on going and, eventually, they get to Geirrod's house and Loki's like, "Hey, this is the place." And then he proceeds to warn Thor that there's actually one dude in the house, but he has

---

[137]   The *Skáldskaparmál* identifies this giantess as Gjalp, one of the daughters of Geirrod.
[138]   In the *Skáldskaparmál*, Thor struggles to reach the other side, and only does so by clinging onto a rowan tree, and, eventually, pulling himself and a worthless Loki to safety.

Sitting in a chair such as this one from the Gåra stave church in Norway can be back-breaking work, quite literally.

a bunch of daughters and they're all real attractive so it's okay. And so Thor's thinking, "Well, that's not exactly what you said earlier," but he knows he can't do anything about it at this point, and so he goes in with Loki, and they're greeted by Geirrod who has one of his minions show them out to the goat shed where they're supposed to stay for the night which sounds like shit but wasn't really all that bad since Thor really likes goats.

So Thor and Loki each take a seat out in this goat shed when the chairs below them start to rumble and then start to fucking levitate! Now Thor does not like this one fucking bit, and so he uses that walking stick of his to push back against the ceiling, and it's kind of a struggle at first, but then he hears something snap, and the chairs come crashing back down to the ground, and he gets up and he looks under them, and he sees a couple of Geirrod's evil daughters[139] squashed to death, and he's like, "What

---

[139] The *Skáldskaparmál* identifies these daughters of Geirrod as Gjalp (of the menstrual fluid flood fame) and Greip. Both similarly die in that version: in agony, their backs broken beyond repair thanks to the mighty strength of Thor.

the fuck, Loki?! These girls look like they got beat with the ugly stick—fucking double-beat even!" So now his temper's starting to flare-up, and Loki's starting to sweat bullets and is trying to eye an escape route before the thunder storm starts when another one of Geirrod's minions shows up and calls the two guys back to the main house for some contests, which kind of diffused the whole situation since Thor's super competitive and likes showing off.

So now they get back to the main house, and as soon as they enter, Geirrod pulls a burning hot ember from out of the fucking fireplace with his tongs, and he throws the thing straight at Thor's head! Well, this is Thor we're talking about here. FUCKING THOR!!! So, of course, he catches it with those special gloves he'd acquired earlier, and he chucks the thing right back at Geirrod, and it kills him right there on the fucking spot. And then he goes looking for all the hot giant ladies, but doesn't find even a single one since all of Geirrod's daughters are super fucking trollish, and Loki's a lying sack of shit, and I still don't have a fucking clue as to why Thor even bothered to stay friends with him after this one.

Only Foolish Gods Ride
the Green Line*

Now I don't have a fucking clue as to why Thor's still hanging out with Loki ever since he fucked him over so fucking hard the last time around, but he still is, and so this one day the two of them decide to go to the aquarium to look at the penguins. I mean, these guys are Norse gods after all, and so it's only natural that they'd want to go look at some aquatic life and shit, but they live up near the Arctic, so they're only used to seeing puffins and seagulls and things like that that live up there but not penguins since they're from the South Pole, and who doesn't like to look at the penguins? Those little guys are fucking cute.

So Loki persuades Thor to drive them both into town together on his goat-mobile since his own piece of shit Oldsmobile's failing to start again, and so it's in the shop getting fixed. But Loki's a total fucking back seat driver, and so he just keeps telling poor Thor exactly how to steer his goats and which roads to take, and so Thor's just going along with it, and, eventually, he ends up following Loki's advice and parking over at the Riverside stop parking lot since Loki thinks it'd be a better idea for them to take the T[140] in the rest of the way.

---

140 A short-hand colloquialism for the MBTA (Massachusetts Bay Transportation Authority), "the T" specifically refers to the

* This myth is the ninth of nine found in The Impudent Edda
that is not attested to in either of the Elder Eddas
or other medieval source material.

The New England Aquarium was once visited by Thor and Loki, who subjected themselves to the horrors of the T's Green Line just to view the penguins. It is said to have been both one of the happiest and one of the most frustrating days in the gods' lives.

So Thor goes ahead and he parks the goats, and they get out of the carriage and go on up to the platform and wait for the T, and then they proceed to just fucking stand there for a long fucking time since Loki directed them to the Green Line.[141] Now Thor's

subway component of the Boston area's multimodal public transit system. The Riverside station is located about ten miles west of downtown Boston in the leafy suburb of Newton.

[141] Boston's subway system's lines are organized by color. The Green Line connects the western suburbs with downtown. The system also consists of the Red Line, the Blue Line, the Orange Line, and the Silver Line, which isn't an actual subway line but

not what one would call a patient individual, and this time he's having an even harder time keeping his shit together since he's so excited to see the fucking penguins, and so he's getting agitated and he's starting to pout, and he's on the verge of throwing a major fucking thunderstorm temper tantrum when the train finally shows up and they get on it, and they ride the fucking thing for the next fucking hour or so.

Now, eventually, they get downtown and walk over to the aquarium where they proceed to spend the whole afternoon, watching the penguins and touching the manta rays and watching the seals swim and do flips and shit, and all and all, they're have a wicked good time, but then it's time for the aquarium to close, and so they have to leave, and so they head back on over to Government Center[142] to catch the T back.

So now they're standing there with tons of other people waiting on the D finger[143] when a C train comes by and a few people get on it, and then that train leaves. Then a few minutes later another C train comes by. And then a few minutes after that a B train comes by. And then an E train. And then another B train and then another E train and then fucking three more goddamned C trains, and all the while Thor's starting to seriously flip the fuck out. Like, I mean he's pacing around the station, screaming bloody murder at the top of his lungs, and waving his hammer

---

rather a sub-par bus line that connects with the actual subway train lines.

[142] Government Center is one of the major T stops in downtown Boston. It takes its name after Boston City Hall, an intensely brutalist and unwelcoming concrete building that lies adjacent to the T stop.

[143] The T's notorious Green Line splits into four distinct branches at its western periphery. Named the B, C, D, and E branches, there is never any rhyme or reason regarding their interrelated timing and circulation patterns from the perspective of the average passenger. The former A branch was replaced by MBTA bus service in 1969.

around like a fucking maniac, but no one seems to care. No one seems to even fucking notice. They're all just standing there sipping their cups of DD,[144] ignoring the guy because he's just another fucking freak waiting on the train, and they've all seen this shit before.

And meanwhile, Loki's going around creeping out all the younger ladies by getting too close to them and sneaking up on them from behind and breathing down their necks and then asking them creepy questions, that sort of thing.

But anyway, eventually, the D train shows up at some point and everyone gets on, and they're all crammed in there like a bunch of fucking sardines, and so now some poor girl's got Thor's armpit in her face, and Loki, of course, has positioned himself in the middle of a group of young college women, and so now they can't get away since the occupancy on the whole damn train's exceeded code nine times over already, and everyone's completely fucking miserable but also pretty much entirely used to it since that's how it goes.

---

[144] A colloquialism for Dunkin' Donuts, which was founded in Quincy, Massachusetts. Due to general misguidance and a marketing executive's ego-driven desire to make a mark, the company formally changed its name to simply Dunkin' in recent years.

Brady Gets Suspended
(*featuring the* Díkbonatal)

So now Thor and Loki get back to Asgard, and they're feeling all frazzled after that whole fucking ordeal on the Green Line, and Odin comes out the front door and is like, "Hey, where you guys been?! You guys are missing out on all the fun. Everyone else is out back right now throwing shit at Brady[145] since nothing can ever hurt him since he's miraculous and the best fucking quarterback of all time."

And so, of course, Thor's like, "Shit! That sounds fucking awesome!" and he runs right out back—and Loki follows him—to where everyone else is throwing shit at Brady.

Now, I mean, they're throwing all sorts of shit at Brady. He's getting fucking axes and kitchen sinks and buckets of nails thrown at him, fucking coffee cups, fucking lobster traps. Hell, I think one guy even threw an entire fucking airplane jet engine at the guy, but nothing even so much as fucking scrapes him since he's just that good.

---

[145] As discussed earlier in the footnote 93 regarding the myth, *The Mistreatment of a Deviant's Ballsack*, the ancient tradition of the fair god, Balder, has been subsumed and hybridized with the newer tradition of the New England Patriots' god, Tom Brady, in *The Impudent Edda*. Additionally, it should be noted that *The Impudent Edda* was recorded in 2019 while Tom Brady still played for the New England Patriots. One must wonder what archaic commentary the anonymous poet might have used to describe Brady if he had orated his Edda after Brady's ignomious defection to Tampa Bay.

Now the reason Brady was getting all this shit thrown at him is that he was having all these wicked bad nightmares about getting injured on the field, which freaked the guy out, and so he went and he told Odin and everyone else about it. So at that point, all the gods—they did the whole shrink thing for him for a while, but then they decided that the best thing to do in this particular situation would be to have Frigg go around the whole wide world and have every living and non-living thing in existence swear to never ever ever ever ever hurt Brady ever.[146] And Frigg didn't mind doing this any since Brady's her kid and all, and she's got natural motherly protective instincts, and so she went around and she got every single animate and inanimate object in existence to swear to not ever harm Brady.[147]

Which means that all the gods basically think that he's completely in-fucking-vincible now, which is why they all started

------

[146]   The council of the gods and its resolution for Frigg to extract promises of non-injury from inanimate objects also occurs in *The Prose Edda*'s *Gylfaginning*, while *Baldrs Draumar*, an ancient Norse poem not found in the original medieval manuscript of *The Poetic Edda* but usually included with modern translations of it, instead describes Odin going on a journey to Hel where he resurrects a dead seeress who then reveals the dire portent of Brady/Balder's bad dreams.

[147]   In one of the more bizarre scientific undertakings of the ancient Nordic myths, Frigg conducted a very large-scale alchemical experiment on all matter in the known universe in which, under presumably highly stringent laboratory conditions, she manipulated the molecular structures of each and every test sample to enhance their properties of inertness. Rather than attempting to create the monetarily valuable element of gold from ordinary ore, as was frequently the aim of ancient alchemical scientists, her hypothesis instead sought to determine whether every known substance could be altered to acquire the neutral qualities associated with the noble gases, the idea being that elements that exhibit such properties of non-reactivity would be least likely to react with and detrimentally alter the chemical composition of Brady/Balder's divine molecular structure.

tossing empty beer bottles and shit at the guy since nothing can hurt him, right? So, like, that sharpened hockey skate that Skadi just threw at him? Fucking just bounced right off his fucking face without so much as leaving a scratch. Same thing with that commuter rail train that Thor chucked at his head...

...I think Frey pry threw a fucking baculum at the guy...[148]

A baculum, well, it's like a walrus dick bone. I mean, that's just the type of thing Frey'd do, you know? Guy's got a one-track mind; he can't stop thinking about dicks. But, you know, it's not like I'm assuming poor Brady liked having some fucking three foot long fossilized walrus dick bone thrown at his head. I mean, even if you're fucking invincible, who wants a fucking walrus dick bone thrown at their head?

Fucking, like, in Alaska they polish and decorate these dick bones and use them as tools and magic wands and shit. I mean, they're supposed to be highly revered or something by the Alaskan aboriginals...

I don't know!

I'm not some sort of dick bone expert. Go ask a fucking barnie.[149] I bet they fucking love dick bones over at Harvard. They're all about showing throbbing crimson shafts a whole lot of love over there.[150]

---

[148]   This line demarcates the start of *The Impudent Edda*'s poetic aside known as the *Díkbonatal* ("The Delineation of the Dick Bones") in which the anonymous poet detours from the main narrative of the myth for a tangential discourse about certain gods' attitudes toward walrus bacculi, as well as Thor and Loki's numerous, ill-fated attempts to purchase liquor in New Hampshire. While not crucial to the events described in the current myth, an editorial decision was made to maintain the *Díkbonatal* in this edition of *The Impudent Edda* because of its seamless and artful transition linking the narrative of the target practice games involving Brady to the narrative of Loki's subsequent traiterous behavior.

[149]   This word is derogatory, local slang for, among other usages, a Harvard University student.

[150]   Here, the anonymous poet has constructed an artful and

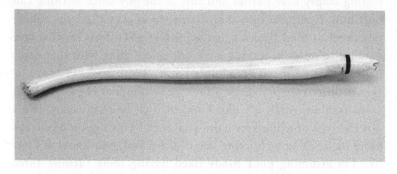

According to The Impudent Edda's *poetic aside known as the* Díkbonatal, *Frey threw a walrus dick bone at Brady. This image depicts a particularly ornate walrus dick bone known as an oosik. An oosik is a dick bone—not necessarily of that of a walrus—that has been polished, carved, or otherwise made decorative by native Alaskan culture. This particular oosik features a groovy polar bear head carved into one end.*

They might also love dick bones over at MIT, too, who knows? Who the fuck even cares?

But you know what? I'll tell you who doesn't love dick bones. Thor.

Thor DOES NOT love dick bones. Unless it's his own, then I believe he makes a very special exception.

I mean, it's just that Thor does not strike me as the type of guy who'd be standing outside of Fenway Park scalping dick bones to passers-by as way to pocket some extra cash. I honestly—I just don't see the guy hoarding up dick bones no matter how hard up he might be at any given time, like, you know, when Loki fucks him over, which happens basically every other day!

---

subtle insult because Harvard's official color is crimson. Crimson also serves as the title of the university's official student newspaper and the ambiguous mascot/name of its athletic teams.

Yeah, like all the times Thor drives his goats up to New Hampshire to stock up on liquor[151] and takes Loki along with him, which always fucks everything up since Loki's a motherfucking shape-shifting demon sack of shit, and he usually just ends up transforming himself into some underage kid with a wicked bad fake ID just to fuck with poor Thor when they get there.

I swear, this happens ALL THE FUCKING TIME.

I mean every time Thor is like, "YES!!! THIS TIME I'M GOING TO FINALLY FUCKING DO IT!" thinking, you know, that he's going to buy all the hard liquor in the entire fucking state of New Hampshire, Loki just then goes and transforms himself into some pimple faced teenage kid, and now they won't sell to Thor no more since he's accompanied by a fucking minor, and I don't know why Thor keeps taking him along all the time...

And don't get me wrong, Thor's a great guy and all, it's just sometimes he's a bit slow.

But Loki, though, he's always been a prick.

Oh and fuck, he just only gets worse because while the gods are all out in the backyard throwing shit at Brady and having a good time, Loki's just getting kind of pissed since good times make him angry since he's an asshole.

So he goes and he asks Frigg, "Hey Frigg, what the fuck? Why isn't anything hurting Brady any? Isn't there anything that can still hurt Brady?"[152]

---

[151] This is an obscure reference to the tendency of Massachusetts residents to cross the border into New Hampshire for the purpose of purchasing of liquor. New Hampshire operates a state-owned monopoly on the sale of all alcoholic beverages stronger than beer or wine while simultaneously charging no sales tax for anything (not just liquor) purchased within its borders. For comparison's sake, one of Massachusetts' nicknames is Taxachusetts.

[152] According *The Prose Edda*'s *Gylfaginning*, Loki breaks his molecular symmetry and alters his mass to rearrange his constituent god particles into the form of an unknown elderly woman so that Frigg does not recognize him when he approaches her

*The Liquor and Wine Outlet in Hampton, New Hampshire.
It is only one of several New Hampshire state-owned and
operated booze stores near the Massachusetts border wherein
Thor has failed to purchase tax-free alcohol thanks to the
devious trickery of Loki.*

And Frigg, she just goes ahead and she tells him! Can you believe that?!

She's just like, "Oh, well, I only ever asked a fully fucking in-
flated football to promise not to hurt him, but I never bothered
to go and find a fucking deflated one and then extract the same
promise out of it."[153]

---

and inquires about Brady/Balder's invincibility. The poet of *The
Impudent Edda* quite openly despises Loki, and it is unlikely that
it was an unintentional oversight that Loki is not presented here
with the degree of cleverness or caution that a disguise would
have implied in this version of the myth.

[153]   This particular aspect of the myth has evolved substantially
since the time of the Elder Eddas. While *The Poetic Edda* itself
does not explicitly discuss Frigg's role of extracting promises from
animate and inanimate objects as *The Prose Edda* does, both of the
Elder Eddas concur that the illicit object in question in the older

So now Loki goes and he gets himself a football, and then he starts deflating the thing, and then he sees Hod, who's just sitting on the bench since he's only a back-up god, basically on the fucking farm team, and no one's really paying any attention to him or any of the other minor league guys. So Loki goes up to him, and he asks him why he's not playing. And Hod's just like, "Because I'm fucking blind as a bat, you fucking dipshit."

And then Loki's like, "Oh shit, man, I'm sorry. Well, here, I'll help you guide your hand if you want to go in for a shift." And so Hod's like, "Yeah, okay, sure," since he's been missing out and, obviously, throwing shit at Brady is the most fun they've had in Asgard since the time when they all stood around and watched Loki get fucked by a horse.

So now Hod steps up to the plate with Loki who helps him toss this deflated piece of shit football at Brady, and the next thing you know, Indianapolis[154] is throwing a fucking shit fit, and Brady's getting the blame for Loki's treachery, and that fucking fire demon, Goodell,[155] sends him down to Hel for a fucking four game suspension, and there ain't even a valkyrie in sight to escort him since he didn't even fall in a real battle.

---

tradition of the mythology was the little plant known as mistletoe and not a partially deflated football. The symbolic significance of the deflated football within the local lore of New England should be apparent to anyone with a modicum of familiarity with the Patriots' NFL franchise. The history that gave rise to this legend is itself too lengthy and convoluted to describe here, but readers unfamiliar with it are encouraged to conduct an internet search for the term "Deflategate."

154   The Deflategate controversy also involved the Indianapolis Colts.

155   NFL Commissioner, Roger Goodell, has apparently taken on the role traditionally occupied by Surt, the fire giant, in *The Impudent Edda*'s rendition of ancient Scandinavian religious beliefs. Goodell was not a popular man in New England at the time of Deflategate.

So all the rest of the gods are just stunned speechless except for Odin who's just like, "You got to be fucking kidding me!" since he hates bullshit, and Goodell's starting to try and wield power like he thinks he's an actual fucking god himself.[156]

---

[156] The ancient poem, *Baldrs Draumar*, also reveals that Hod not only kills his brother Brady/Balder, but that upon having done so, Odin retaliates by having sex with a giantess named Rind, who one day later gives birth to Odin's newest son, Vali, who grows to full manhood in a single day and immediately murders Hod who, being blind, doesn't even see it coming.

Belichick Rides to Hel

So now Frigg hears about Goodell's god-like proclamation, and she's like, "That motherfucking piece of shit!" So she goes and she gets up off her ass and walks over to the locker room where everyone else is standing around staring at the tv screen, watching the coverage of the fucking suspension like it's a goddamned murder scene. So now she sees everyone's just moping around, not knowing what the fuck to do, and so she decides right then and there that she better take control of the whole situation before it gets anymore pathetic, and so she looks them all in the eyes and says, "All right, so which one of you fucking dipshits is going to ride down to Hel to try and appeal for me on Brady's behalf?"

And so that's when Belichick the Bold,[157] who's another one of Odin's bastard sons, tells Frigg, "Yeah, sure, I'll drive down to Hel," since Brady's his star quarterback. And so to help him out a little on his way, Odin gives him the keys to his eight-legged mustang, and so, of course, Belichick thinks this is wicked pisser, and so he jumps behind the wheel and he fires up that beast, and before you even know it, he's peeling out of the parking lot and heading for the rainbow bridge like he thinks he's the second coming of Mario Andretti or some shit.

---

[157]   In *The Impudent Edda*, Belichick the Bold has taken on the role traditionally held by Hermod in *The Prose Edda*'s *Gylfaginning*. As with Brady, his mythological status in *The Impudent Edda* is derived from the legendary status of a member of the New England Patriots—in this case, a coach rather than a player.

Now all the other gods who are lingering back in the locker room decide that maybe they ought to go outside and get some fresh air or something and maybe even fire up the grills and, you know, get some fucking tail-gating action going so as to try and get their minds off of Brady's predicament. So, they're all out there now in the parking lot, grilling and drinking, and things are still kind of somber but at least they're not just standing around moping like they were before when things start to get really fucking weird.

So at this point, some damned giantess riding a fucking wolf gets lost on her way to Rhode Island and decides to pull up next to where the gods are grilling out in the parking lot to ask for directions. Well, four of Odin's berserkers just flip the fuck out because no way some fucking giantess has got the right to crash their fucking funeral tail-gating party, and so they go berserk and fucking kill that wacko right there on the spot, which everyone else thought was wicked good entertainment except for Gisele[158] who just can't handle this degree of senseless violence on top of all the other bullshit that's happened to her husband lately, and so she ends up having a bit of a nervous breakdown, but then Sif starts talking to her about the beaches in Brazil and this helps get her mind off of things at least for a bit.

And all while this is happening, Ole One-Eye's just minding the grill and flipping the burgers, but one of his special rings somehow ends up slipping off of his finger by accident and into the grill and he loses the thing in the flames, which sucks.[159] But the best part

---

[158] *The Impudent Edda* displays a late case of German-Brazilian influence here in its assertion that Brady/Balder's wife is named Gisele rather than the more traditional Nanna, as is the case in the Elder Eddas and other earlier sources. It is quite possible that Gisele's general disapproval of the gods' excessive violence contributed to her decision to divorce Brady in 2022, three full years after the anonymous poet recorded his Edda on the *Codex Bostonia*.

[159] While unnamed, the magic ring in question is most likely Draupnir, which was forged by the dwarf biker gang known as the

of the whole party had to be when some dumb dwarf popped up from out of nowhere, and Thor got all pissed about it and kicked the little bastard straight into the fucking flames![160] HA![161]

But anyway, while all this is going on, Belichick the Bold's made his way down to Hel, and so now he's parking Odin's eight-

---

Hel's Valkyries, as described in the myth, *Wicked Good Dwarf Treasure.*

[160] It is unclear exactly how a dwarf, upon having been kicked by the strongest of the gods, would—despite his small size—still be small enough to fall through one of the gaps in the cooking grate of the grill being manned by Odin. The Norse myths have historically always been full of spatial incongruencies and inconsistences that can best be explained with the unstated use of a transmogrifier, and this instance is no exception.

[161] *The Impudent Edda* deviates substantially from *The Prose Edda* in its relating of the activities immediately following the suspension/death of Brady/Balder, which has traditionally been one of the most somber yet cinematographic events in all of Norse mythology. As related in the *Gylfaginning*, the gods do not start tail-gating at Gillette Stadium in Foxborough, Massachusetts, but rather prepare a ship-borne funeral pyre for the fallen hero. Brady/Balder's boat, however, is of such magnificence and weight that the gods cannot tow it across land (from where it is kept in the off-season) to the water themselves, and so instead they enlist the help of the wolf-riding giantess, Hyrrokkin, who obliges and, notably, does not get murdered by the berserkers, though her wolf does. At this point, Brady/Balder's corpse is carried and placed on the boat while Gisele/Nanna dies from grief and is subsequently laid beside him. The pyre is then lit, and as Thor steps forward to consecrate it with his mighty hammer, a dwarf runs in front of him, which he then kicks into the flames. After Thor's holy consecration of the pyre/ritualistic act of dwarf murder, Odin intentionally places his magic ring, Draupnir, in the flames and Brady/Balder's horse is slaughtered and also placed on the pyre. Finally, with gods, elves, dwarves, valkyries, and even some giants in full attendance, Brady/Balder's boat is pushed out to sea in truly epic viking fashion, burning brightly against the darkening sky as the final doom of the gods looms ever closer.

The Tjäng-videsten from Alskog, Sweden illustrates several motifs from Viking Age era Scandinavian life, most notably the eight-legged won-der-horse known as Sleipnir that Odin allows Be-lichick to borrow for his ride down to Hel.

legged mustang and feeding the fucking meter, and he heads into the Court of Appeals and comes across this cranky receptionist, and she looks at him and she's like, "Hey, what the fuck are you doing here? You don't look like a lawyer to me."

And, of course, Belichik's no fucking lawyer so he's like, "What the fuck?! I'm just looking for my star quarterback, you seen—" But that rude bitch just cuts him off and tells him where he needs to go, and then she goes back to reading about the underworld's thirty-six newest ways to reach orgasm as fast as possible or whatever in her Cosmo magazine. So Belichik gets on the fucking elevator and goes down to the basement like he was instructed to do and then finally finds the door to Hel's office, and he opens it and goes right on in since, he's, like—you know, he's the head coach.

And sure enough, he sees Hel just sitting there in that dingy basement office surrounded by hundreds and hundreds of empty styrafoam DD[162] cups while Brady's just sitting there in a chair off to the side like a little kid in time out next to poor fucking Charlie who never paid his exit fare and has been stuck in this shithole since the fucking '40s. So, Belichik gives Brady a nod and goes straight up to Hel, and he inquires about Brady's fucking fate and Hel's just like, "Eh, he's stuck down here till someone pays the proper fucking exit fare."[163]

And so Belichik tries to give her a nickel since he's heard this song before, but now the goddamned transit authority's gone and jacked up the prices all over again, and so now it's going to cost the gods a lot more than just a fucking five-cent piece just to set Brady free, and this one's not going to be the sort of ticket you can just download on your fucking iphone and then forget about it.[164]

---

[162] As previously noted in footnote 144 in the myth, *Only Foolish Gods Ride the Green Line*, DD is local Bostonian shorthand for Dunkin' Donuts.

[163] In historic Boston lore, Charlie is the fictional folk-hero who gets stuck on the T (the subway), forever doomed to ride beneath the streets of Boston because he didn't have the proper exit fare to disembark. Charlie's plight was first recorded in 1949 in a song by Jacqueline Steiner and Bess Lomas Hawes. The song reached greater popularity with the version recorded by The Kingston Trio in 1959. More recently, Charlie has served as a mascot for the transit system as a whole.

[164] As with the events surrounding Brady/Balder's tail-gate party/funeral, the scene involving Belichick/Hermod's ride to Hel and encounter with the demon woman of the same name deviates drastically from the earlier rendition provided by *The Prose Edda*. The version preserved in the *Gylfaginning* portrays Belichick/Hermod as riding Odin's eight-legged steed, Sleipnir, for nine whole days en route to Hel before he reaches the Gjoll Bridge, which separates the land of the living from the land of the dead. There, he encounters the maiden, Modgud, who inquires about

But if those gods don't figure out how to pay this fucking tax pretty soon then poor Brady's going to end up sitting out more than just the start of the season. But on the upside, he's got poor fucking Charlie there to keep him company, so at least he's not all alone.

his ancestry—since that was always of utmost importance in ancient and medieval times—and also confirms that Brady/Balder rode over the same bridge sometime earlier. Belichick/Hermod then crosses the bridge and continues on the road to Hel till he reaches the Gates of Hel, leaps over them upon Sleipnir, and enters Hel's hall where he sees his brother, Brady/Balder, sitting in the seat of honor, but with no sign of Charlie anywhere. After spending the night, he asks Hel if she would be willing to release his brother, and she responds that she would, but only if every

A subterranean poster depicting the stylish good looks of Charlie. While it has been postulated that he may ride forever beneath the streets of Boston due to an unfortunate incident in which he was unable to pay the proper exit fare back in 1949, the anonymous poet of The Impudent Edda *seems to believe that he is actually being held captive in New York. Either way, his fate is still unlearned, but one thing is certain: he's the man who never returned.*

living and non-living thing in the known universe will weep on Brady/Balder's behalf. Belichick/Hermod prepares to return to Asgard, but before he departs, Brady/Balder gives him the ring, Draupnir, to return to their father, Odin, and Gisele/Nanna (who is dead in *The Prose Edda*'s version of the myth at this point) hands him a robe to give to Frigg, and a gold ring to give to Fulla, the infrequently mentioned goddess whose primary responsibility is to keep Frigg's insanely massive assortment of shoes in order and under control.

Loki Swims with the Fishes

So now poor fucking Brady's trapped in a shitty subway station beneath the Second District Court of Appeals in fucking NEW YORK with that bitch, Hel, and that goofy bastard, Charlie, while Belichick's racing back to Frigg and Odin and all the others so's that he can tell them that they got to convince every damn thing in the whole wide world to cry on Brady's behalf in order to lift the suspension on their star quarterback. And if at first they don't succeed, well, then the entire fucking universe is going to get scorched like a fucking nuclear holocaust since that's the type of hardcore shit that these viking guys believed back in those days.

But the gods, though, they send out these messengers to all over the fucking place, and they're getting everyone and everything to cry for Brady except for this one old giantess[165] who's hiding in a crevice in a granite quarry up in Quebec all alone by herself, and she's pissed at the world, and so she refuses to weep for him since she's a bitch, and you know what that means...

...EVERYTHING IS FUCKED!!!

EVERYTHING!!![166]

---

[165] *The Prose Edda*'s *Gylfaginning* reveals that this giantess' name is especially feminine-sounding: Thokk.

[166] In the original recording of *The Impudent Edda*, the anonymous poet's already questionable sobriety undergoes a marked decrease beginning with this myth, from whence it only continues to further deteriorate until the final seconds of the final myth.

There is no come-back. This is not like game 7 against Toronto back in '13 where miracles really do happen late in the 3rd.[167] I'm telling you, this is more like regular season and not making it to the play-offs at all. But the gods though, they all think that this giantess was actually Loki in disguise which is on account of him being the biggest shit-stick on the planet, and, of course, now he knows that the gods are going to be on his ass like white on rice, and so he takes off and he goes and he finds a hiding place up somewhere deep in the White Mountains.[168] And so as to try and blend in better with his local surroundings, he holes himself up there in some cabin somewhere, and then—get this—he proceeds to turn himself into a fucking fish! Can you believe that? And then, I guess, he just goes swimming in the river[169] out back because, well, he's a fish now...fuck, man...I haven't been fishing in so long...

But fuck Loki though, fuck him. Fuck him, I sweaarrrr...okay, and so sometimes he gets kind of bored with being a fucking fish because, you know, who wants to be a fucking fish, right? I mean, at this point he pry wished he'd stolen Frigg's falcon outfit again,[170] but he didn't think of that in his rush to get out of

---

[167]   On May 13, 2013 the Boston Bruins stunned the Toronto Maple Leafs in game 7 of the first round of the Eastern Conference playoff series. Down 4-1 in the 3rd period, the Bruins rebounded in one of the greatest comebacks of NHL history, winning 5-4 in overtime.

[168]   The mountain range in New Hampshire where Tyr used to enjoy cruising around with Fenrir as related in the myth, *Loki is a Dead-Beat Dad*, as well as home to the tallest mountain in the eastern United States and the original Lyfjaberg mythological medical hospital, as revealed in the myth, *Lyfjaberg Gets Taken by Eminent Domain*.

[169]   According to the *Gylfaginning* in *The Prose Edda*, Loki spends the majority of his time as a fish swimming in the waterfall or rapids (it is unclear which) known as Franang's Falls. This does not contradict *The Impudent Edda*'s version.

[170]   Loki's obsession with avian transmogrifiers apparently con-

*A tranquil northern New England river rapids scene, which
is also where it has been prophesied that Loki will taunt
Thor with his superior aquatic swimming abilities as a fish.*

Asgard. Anyway, being a fish is fucking stupid, and so, of course,
sometimes even Loki's got to take a break from being a fish and
all, and so he goes and he, uhh…well, he basically just sits by his
fireplace where he fantasizes about his own death since he's a sick
fucking bastard, and then for some reason the fucking idiot goes
and he makes a fucking fishing net.

That's right, a fucking fishing net.

So now what we got is Loki just sitting there looking at this
net like it's a fucking noose since for a fish it pretty much fucking
is, which is when the rest of the gods all enter into his house! So

---

tinues right up until the final moments of his exile. For more on
his prior theft of Frigg's falcon transmogrifier, see the myth, *Thor
Wades Through the Menstrual Fluid Fjord.*

he throws the fucking thing into the fire and runs out back where he proceeds to jump back into the river in fish form again.

But the gods, you know, they weren't born yesterday, and so they see the ashes of that net, and they figure it out. They're like, "OH FUCK, LOOK AT THAT. IT'S A FUCKING FISHING NET. LOKI MUST BE SWIMMING LIKE A FISH IN THE RIVER RIGHT NOW. LET'S GO KILL THAT STUPID SON OF A BITCH."[171]

And so they go on out back down to the river, and the gods, they're loving that clean and clear, cool mountain water because it ain't like that murky shit water like we got around here. And also, it means that the gods can actually SEE all those fucking fish THROUGH THE WATER with their OWN EYES.

And so now they're standing there around the fucking river, staring at the fucking water, trying to spot Loki, and there's a fucking ton of fish in the water! And I guess it's got to be that clean, cool mountain air that's good for the fish's lungs or whatever that does it, but you know, it means they got to play a little game of riparian *Where's Waldo* for now since the river's so fucking full of fishes.

And so, as I've been telling you all along, Thor is not exactly what one would call a patient individual. So, like, maybe all the

---

[171]   According to *The Prose Edda*'s *Gylfaginning*, the god that first notices the ashes of the net and recognizes its potential significance is Kvasir, who in *The Impudent Edda*'s version of the mythology is first created from spittle in the myth, *How Not to Get Away with Witch Murder*, and is subsequently murdered by a couple of dwarf gang members in the myth, *Blood Spit Honey Death*. Curiously enough, *The Prose Edda* also states that Kvasir is murdered by dwarves, but provides no explanation as to how he could then still be alive much later in order to help capture Loki. This is most likely an oversight/editing error on Snorri Sturlason's part, but since he was murdered eight hundred years ago, this could not be confirmed at the time of the printing of this edition of *The Impudent Edda*.

other gods are just standing there keeping their cool, counting the fish, but not Thor. Thor's a fucking fighter, and so he's getting himself all worked up into one of his killing moods, and the storm clouds are starting to gather overhead, and so if they don't spot Loki pretty soon so that he can go and open up a full-on can of angry thunder god whoop-ass on Loki, then they better pray to...well, I guess they better pray to themselves. But regardless, they better pray that there's at least a shit-ton of beer back in the fucking fridge because the only thing that stands a chance of appeasing Thor right now other than killing some fucking fish is getting drunk. The guy's a fucking lush.

Snake Poison Torture Time

So now the gods are all just standing around by the fucking river watching Loki swim around like a fucking fish. Which he is, I guess, since he transformed his dumb ass into one, and so now he's doing fucking swan dives and back flips and shit just to egg them all on till Thor finally fucking loses it and just dives in head first after the slippery bastard!

And he's lucky he missed the fucking rocks, too! Not that it would have made any difference if he hadn't, though, since he's already got a fucking whetsone lodged in his skull from some other brawl he got into a while back with some giant asshole.[172] But now he basically snatches that piece of shit, Loki, right out of thin air while he's doing some flippity-flop like some sort of acrobat at the summer Olympics or something, and I tell you, he just

---

[172] While the story of the whetsone lodged in Thor's head only receives passing mention in *The Impudent Edda*, it is described in colorful detail in *The Prose Edda*'s *Skáldskaparmál*. In it, Thor engages in a one-on-one personal duel with the evil giant, Hrungnir. During the climax of this duel, Thor hurls his hammer at Hrungnir, who himself throws his own weapon of choice, a whetstone (an odd choice, but Hrungnir was admittedly a nonconformist), at Thor. The hammer and whetstone collide in mid-air, and while the hammer goes on to strike and kill Hrungnir where he stands, the whetstone breaks into two pieces, one of which strikes Thor in the head, where it has been lodged ever since (the advanced surgical techniques necessary to remove it had not yet been developed at the time of this event).

fucking crushes that motherfucker's tail right then and there with
his bare hands, and now this is the reason why all the Norwegians
think that salmon's got narrow tails...[173]

...but yeah, so now we got Thor who's thinking it'd be a wicked good idea to fucking flay Loki alive right then and there on
the fucking spot since he loves violence and the immediate gratification that goes along with killing, but NNNOOOOOOOO.
All the other gods are like, "Uh, we can't do that Thor, we need to
fucking torture his ass instead." And FOR THOR THIS FUCK-
ING SUCKS!!! I mean, for him this is like...uh, well, it's like
uh...uh...well, it's like losing the signal on your cell phone, I
guess. And you know, not being able to update your status for
the rest of the day since it's, you know—it's all about the instant
gratification and the petty distraction that makes you feel like
your life has some semblance of meaning. But as a way to try and
appease Thor, since he's got a nasty fucking temper, the rest of
the gods give him a couple of kegs of stout since it's Saint Patty's
Day[174] and all, and he loves getting shit-faced as much as every
other red-haired bastard in this fucking town.

So now the gods, they all go and they lock Loki up in a
fucking cave somewhere out in the middle of fucking I-don't-
even-know-where, and it doesn't even matter except for the fact

---

[173]   *The Prose Edda*'s *Gylfaginning*'s version of this myth relates
a much more elaborate and highly orchestrated effort to capture
Loki that involved all of the gods (not just Thor) and a special
net that they had expressly made for this purpose. Loki attempts
to jump over the net and is captured by Thor mid-air, somewhat
similar to his capture as portrayed in *The Impudent Edda*'s rendition.

[174]   The fact that Loki's capture occurred on March 17th is a
very new and important detail that has never before been revealed
in any of the earlier Eddic sources. Likewise, Saint Patrick's role
in *The Impudent Edda* is a previously unbeknownst detail that
sheds new light on the origins of the snake that Skadi keeps in her
possession as described in this myth.

that Thor's not there since he's already finished off his kegs of Guinness and has moved onto binge-drinking green-colored Budweisers with the guys from the BC hockey team who are still celebrating their victory over BU at all the touristy spots around Faneuil Hall.[175] And so he's off acting like a fucking hooligan or whatever with the cool kids[176] and...uh...well, the rest of the gods kidnap Loki's normal sons,[177] and they fucking transform one of them into a fucking wolf, and you know what this wolf does? He fucking murders Loki's other normal son! He fucking MURDERS him!

I don't know why. Because it's what wolves who used to be people are supposed to do?

Well, it's what the gods wanted...I mean, obviously, this was intentional on their part because next thing you know, they take

---

[175] Faneuil Hall is a historic marketplace located in downtown Boston and a prime destination for tourists to the city. Additionally, BC and BU refer, respectively, to Boston College and Boston University. The rivalry between the two schools' hockey teams is nearly as ancient as Odin's inappropriate lust for women who are only a mere fraction of his age.

[176] Beginning here, *The Impudent Edda* deviates from all other sources regarding Thor's behavior and whereabouts following Loki's capture. The Elder Eddas generally concur that Thor continued to keep the company of his fellow Aesir, rather than going off solo on an all-night bender in downtown Boston in the final days leading up to the collective doom that eventually destroys them all.

[177] *The Prose Edda*'s *Gylfaginning* reveals that Loki's sons are named Vali and Nari/Narfi (Snorri appears to have been confused about the exact spelling of the second son) while the *Lokasenna* in *The Poetic Edda* reveals that the names are Nari (rather than Vali) and Narfi; the two Elder Eddas do not agree on this particular matter nor on the specific events. The *Lokasenna*'s version does not involve one brother-turned-wolf ripping the other brother to shreds. The *Lokasenna* does, however, concur that one was turned into a wolf while the other was gutted (but without any specific details as to how).

The New England Holocaust Memorial in downtown Boston. It has been foretold that Thor will vomit all over himself and pass out drunk beneath its glass towers during the events immediately preceding Ragnarök.

that poor kids' entrails, and they fucking tie Loki up with them and...yeah, these are the good guy gods we're talking about!

...I mean, yeah, I know Loki's a real piece of shit, but goddamn.

So next, Skadi just so happens to have this poisonous snake with her that she's carried around all over the place ever since Patty boy chased the fucking thing out of Ireland and...aahhhh, I'm not sure when that was, but I think it was a long while back. It's a whole different story altogether.

Anyway, I guess, you just never know when you might need to have a poisonous snake on hand to torture someone with, and in this case, it turned out to come in pretty handy. I mean, it's fucking practical! If you're looking to torture a demonic Norse god anyway, that is. But yeah, so Skadi, she goes and she, like, she somehow, like, drapes the fucking thing over a rock right there above Loki's head, and, I guess, it just stays there...like, it doesn't even try to slither away or anything...

I don't know! Maybe Patty boy hit it too hard on the head with his fucking shillelagh or something? I don't know.

But now it's got a fucking mental defect or something. I mean, the dumb thing just lays there without ever even moving, and, basically, it just sits there and fucking drools burning hot venom down all over Loki's fucking face for the rest of eternity, except for, you know, when the entire fucking world ends in a huge fucking fireball of death and destruction at the end of time.

But also his wife, Sigyn, helps him out most of the time by catching the poison drool in a bowl which is pretty nice of her since she doesn't have to be there, and she's missing the parade down Broadway[178] on account of this shit.[179]

But poor fucking Thor, man! That guy! What a fucking guy. So he's also drooling right now but that's only on account of the fact that he's passed out face down on one the steam vents over at the Holocaust Memorial[180] after he got himself kicked out of

---

[178]   This is an oblique reference to South Boston's Saint Patrick's Day parade.

[179]   *The Impudent Edda* bypasses a powerful detail here that is fortunately not lost in either of the Elder Eddas: that whenever Sigyn leaves Loki's side to empty the bowl of poisonous venom, the venom that drips down upon his face in the interim results in extreme pain. With each drop that splashes on his face, Loki thrashes violently, and his convulsions form the origins of all the earthquakes that occur in Middle-Earth. As with Old Norse astrophysics, the science behind Old Norse geotectonics deviates dramatically from our current, prevailing understandings of natural phenomena.

[180]   Designed by Stanley Saitowitz, the New England Holocaust Memorial commemorates the Jewish victims of the Holocaust.

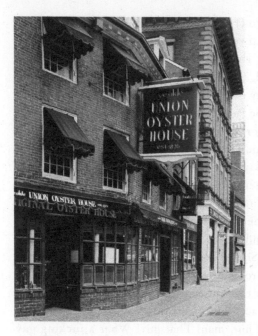

The oldest restaurant in the United States and the unfortunate scene of Thor's disgraceful and highly inebriated pre-Ragnarök vomiting fiasco.

the Oyster House for puking all over JFK's honorary table...[181] and yeah, now the guy's being a fucking vagrant like Odin. Jesus Christ. At least when Loki was around, he didn't drink himself to fucking oblivion, but at the same time, he really fucking knows how to get into the spirit of the holiday. I think he even wore a green cape this time.

---

[181]   The Union Oyster House in Boston is the United States' oldest restaurant. The restaurant was frequented by John F. Kennedy, and a special plaque commemorates the booth where he regularly dined.

Thor Breaks and Enters into a Dunkin' Donuts

So like I was telling you, Thor's been passed out, you know, just sleeping it off under some wicked deep pile of snow on the side of the road since fucking Saint Patty's Day, but then he finally wakes the fuck up because now his stomach's starting to growl, and he needs to eat some food for his fucking hangover. So he digs himself out of his snow mound, and he goes and he stumbles on over to the nearest street corner to get his food, but then it turns out that the DD[182] is FUCKING CLOSED SINCE THE ENTIRE FUCKING CITY'S SHUTDOWN BECAUSE IT'S SNOWING LIKE A BITCH OUTSIDE!

Now, naturally, this is some real heart-breaking news for poor Thor since he's fucking starving, but just to be clear, he doesn't give a rat's ass about the snow. This is fucking Thor we're talking about here! FUCKING THOR!!! HE FUCKING THRIVES ON THIS SHIT. ICE, SNOW, SLUSH, ROAD SALT, MUD SEASON, FUCKING WHATEVER...I MEAN, HE'S FUCKING FROM THE LAND OF THE ICE AND SNOW...AND HIS HAMMER WILL DRIVE OUR SHIPS TO NEW LANDS!!! TO FIGHT THE HORDE, SINGING AND CRYING, VALLL-HALLLLAAAAAAA, I AM COMING!!!![183]

---

[182]   As previously noted in footnote 144, this is a colloquialism for Dunkin' Donuts.

[183]   While such instances occur with much less frequency in *The Impudent Edda* than is found in older sources, the recitation of an earlier, related work (usually in poetic format) known to the author is a common convention in Eddic literature. In this case,

Sometimes you just got to get the led out, you know?

But in terms of tempers, fucking no one tops Thor. Fucking no one. He's got an even shorter fuse than Terry O'Reilly,[184] but he doesn't have to go and climb over the boards just to start a fucking fight with the fans because he's got to couple of demented goats that'll do all the climbing for him. And he can fucking whip out Mjölnir whenever the fuck he feels like!

NO!!!

Mjölnir is not his dick. It's his hammer.

HIS HAMMER IS NAMED MJÖLNIR.

I don't know what his dick is named. Maybe Thor Jr.? Or Spicy Ginger? Or how about Lil' Thunderstick? You know, since he's the thunder god and all...

...well, I don't know, but could be, being as he's a fucking ginger and all...yeah, Hollywood got that one WAY FUCKING OFF. Fucking morons.

Well, yeah, so he's fucking starving since he ain't eaten since he blacked out back in March, and so now he whips out his Mjölnir so as to break into the fucking DD.

Because he wants to eat all the breakfast sandwiches! The guy's fucking starving! I TOLD YOU THIS ALREADY. He ain't eaten since March, and he doesn't give a flying fuck about organic or locally grown whatever. He just wants a GODDAMNED BREAKFAST SANDWICH IS ALL. And also maybe a donut or two.

Yeah, so he uses his magic hammer—NOT HIS DICK—to

---

while it goes unstated in specific terms by the poet himself, he is drawing upon verses attributed to the great 20th century English skald, Robert Plant.

184   Beginning with this comment about Terry O'Reilly (a lovable goon who played for the "Big Bad" Boston Bruins in the 1970s and early 1980s), the anonymous poet begins to reference Boston sports lore with increasing frequency. Some of these artful allusions are generally considered to be common knowledge; some are obscure. The footnotes of this volume do not attempt to clarify each and every instance of Boston sports lore that the poet references.

The Dunkin' Donuts on North Street in Boston facing the historic Faneuil Hall marketplace. It is here that Thor will commit petty larceny after waking up on the street with a massive hangover.

break and enter into the DD like a fucking delinquint, but then he realizes that he doesn't know how to operate the special oven, and all the sandwiches are frozen fucking solid, and so he sits his ass down, and he starts crying and, eventually, he falls to sleep and so now he's laying there on the floor, snoozing like some homeless bastard when his archnemesis the Middle-Earth Demon Serpent Snake, or whatever the fuck that thing is, suddenly wakes up and rises up from OUT OF THE OCEAN. And next thing you know, this goddamned degenerate reptile's slithering his way on up to shore over at Revere Beach[185] so he can fill up

---

[185]   The same waterfront location where Odin and his otherwise

on some roast beef sandwiches before starting on his killing spree downtown.

Now this would not have happened had Thor gotten the fucking nourishment he needed! THOR FUCKIN' RUNKIN ON DUNKIN!!! Or something like that...I don't know, but sounds good, right? Shit, I bet that slogan'd sure as hell sell some extra donuts if you ask me.

But yeah, so the poor fucking guy's passed out from malnourishment, and so now there's no one to stop the fucking snake, who's at this point barreling down 1A[186] like he's running late for a fucking flight. Now at the EXACT same time as this, Loki's other jerk-off son, the Fenriswolf, busts out of his ribbon-chains from up off the coast of Maine somewhere, and so now that guy's driving down 95[187] like a fucking whackjob in zero visibility whiteout conditions because the snow's coming down like a fucking bitch.[188] And not that it really matters anyways since no one can

---

do-nothing brothers created the first man and woman. Revere Beach is also the location where Kelly's Roast Beef, a Massachusetts dining establishment, first opened its doors in 1951.

[186]   A state freeway that runs north-south along the Massachusetts coast and that also serves as one of the primary thoroughfares for reaching Boston Logan International Airport.

[187]   Short for I-95, the major north-south vehicular transporation corridor along the east coast of the United States, connecting Maine to Florida.

[188]   While most of this myth does not have a direct correlation in either of the Elder Eddas, at this point in his telling it is presumed that the anonymous poet is introducing the well-known Fimbulwinter, which is attested to in both of the earlier Eddas. The Fimbulwinter constitutes six extreme winters in uninterrupted succession that precede Ragnarök. During the Fimbulwinter, brother will kill brother, and father will kill son. The wolf, Skoll, will swallow the sun and the wolf, Månegarm, will swallow the moon, spattering blood across the sky and obscuring the stars which will then disappear from view. In the words of The Poetic Edda's Völuspá, it is an axe-age, a blade-age, a wind-age, and a

see them anymore anyway due to the fucking blizzard conditions out there, but another couple of wolves just jumped up from out of fucking nowhere and swallowed the sun and the moon, so now the sky's just all totally gone to shit. And to really fucking top it all off, down over at South Station,[189] the Amtrak crashes into the commuter rail and lets loose a shit-ton of asshole New Yorkers[190] who are now starting to swarm the city like a fucking plague.[191]

---

wolf-age, and none shall be spared. The earth will tremble, trees will wither, and mountains will fall as the impending doom of the gods now very rapidly approaches.

[189] One of Boston's two major train stations. South Station serves the trains that depart to and arrive from points further south, including New York City. The commuter rail serves the greater Boston metropolitan area (including Rhode Island) while the Amtrak service connects Boston to destinations beyond Massachusetts and Rhode Island.

[190] An ancient and timeless rivalry exists between Boston and New York. Much of this rivalry in the present-day may be attributed to the century-old friction between the Boston Red Sox and the New York Yankees. In 1919 Babe Ruth left the Red Sox for the Yankess, and Boston experienced its subsequent "Curse of the Bambino." However, the rivalry extends deeper into history than that, reaching back to the American colonial era when Boston's mother state of Great Britain and New York's (New Amsterdam's) mother state of the Netherlands were competing for dominance in the New World. Britain won, but New York eventually surpassed Boston as the financial and business hub of the U.S.

[191] With this sequence of events, Ragnarök has officially begun. While *The Impudent Edda* generally follows the older tradition set forth in the Elder Eddas regarding the Fenriswolf's escape from his bonds, and the Middle-Earth Serpent's emergence from the sea, it deviates drastically in its depiction of the train full of invasive New Yorkers. The Elder Eddas instead relate that the sons of Muspellsheim, evil fire giants, will split asunder the sky as they descend upon the field of battle to bring death and destruction to all.

Everyone and Everything Dies

So now as if having all these goddamned Yankees fans prowling around town's not bad enough, just to make matters even worse, some shitty ass boat made out of a bunch of decayed toenails[192] docks over next to the aquarium and lets loose the entire squad of those jerk-off Habs[193] while at the same time that fucking fire demon, Roger Goodell,[194] jumps up from out of the sewers covered in piss and shit and starts marching down Charles Street flinging flaming feces like a deranged monkey since he's such a sick and twisted fuck. And so, of course, Loki sees this shit, and he's like, "If that fucking douchebag can manipulate the system and get away with it, then so can I since I'm an actual evil fucking god," and so then he goes and he breaks his magical chains and escapes from that dark cave up there somewhere in New Hampshire and ends up hitchhiking his ass back all the way into town.

So now you got this horrible situation where all these fucking freaks are starting to converge on the Common,[195] and Heimdall,

---

192 The Elder Eddas have identified this ship as Naglfar.

193 A nickname for the Montréal Canadiens, longtime rivals of the Boston Bruins. According to the Elder Eddas, Naglfar is crewed by evil frost giants, not professional hockey players from Quebec.

194 While universally vilified for good reason by the New England populace, Roger Goodell's role in the Twilight of the Gods has traditionally been held by the fire giant named Surt.

195 Boston Common, as previously seen in Odin's decrepit wandering through downtown Boston in the myth, *Odin Experiments with Public Vagrancy.*

Several manholes at an intersection on Charles Street in the Beacon Hill neighborhood. It is from one of these that the evil fire giant known as Goodell will emerge from the sewers, flinging shit, and usher in the beginning of the Twilight of the Gods.

who's supposed to be on the lookout for this type of shit's too busy burying his sorrows into pint after fucking pint of Harpoon IPA over at at his favorite Irish pub on Beacon Street instead of standing out in front of the Freedom Trail[196] visitor center in his colonial attire like he ought to have been, finally sees that goddamned serpent slither right on past the window outside, and he just about shits a brick, but then he runs and he gets his special horn,[197] and

---

[196]   The Freedom Trail is a walking trail that connects Boston's numerous historic sites. 2.5 miles in length, the trail is itself marked on the ground with strips of brick pavement or paint on asphalt.
[197]   *The Prose Edda*'s *Gylfaginning* reveals that this horn is called the Gjallarhorn. The imagery of Heimdall's blowing of the Gjal-

he starts blowing on it like the fucking British are coming so as to
wake Odin the fuck up since that guy's been sleeping it off over
on the stoop in front of The Asgard on Mass Ave[198] after he got
shit-faced there the night before and sent Freyja a whole fucking
barrage of drunken dick pics.

So now everyone's woken up and's getting ready, and all the
gods are gearing up in their best suits of armor, and Bobby Orr
and Big Papi and Gronk and all the rest of Odin's guys are lacing
up in the locker room, and pretty soon they're all starting to storm
out of The Meadhall's five hundred and forty doors[199] straight on
towards the river, and they're all crossing the bridge now, and
so they meet up with Odin and Heimall and all the other gods
outside of MGH,[200] and together they all start walking towards
the Common, and Odin's in the lead right next to Ray Bourque
who's still carrying the Cup,[201] but Odin, he thought he'd mix it
up a bit for the occasion so instead of the usual wizard robe, he's
wearing a Patriots jersey with his Gandalf hat in honor of Brady,

---

larhorn is recreated in altered but spectacular detail in the final
battle of *The Two Towers* film when Gimli the dwarf blows into
the horn at Helm's Deep as the tide of the battle for Rohan's
existence turns.

[198]   Local shorthand slang for Massachusetts Avenue. The former
Irish Pub known as The Asgard was previously encountered in the
myth, *Middle-Earth is Just an Eyelash on the Celestial Gallows Pole*.

[199]   The meadhall in question is known as Valhalla, the hall of
the slain, in the Elder Eddas, and the heroes who rush out of its
five hundred and forty doors (the specific quantity is affirmed by
the *Grímnismál* in *The Poetic Edda*) are known as the Einherjar,
Odin's own personal troop of undead warriors whose souls have
been plucked up by the valkyries upon their death in battle on the
human plane of existence in Middle-Earth. Coincidentally, there
is also a restaurant named the Meadhall that appropriately serves
mead in Cambridge, Massachusetts.

[200]   The same hospital where Menglad's nurses once worked as
related in the myth, *Lyfjaberg Gets Taken by Eminent Domain*.

[201]   The Stanley Cup.

The Asgard bar in Cambridge before its fateful permanent closure. It is from beneath this sign that Odin will drunkenly and relentlessly send Freyja dick pics on the eve of Ragnarök.

who's still having to sit this one out since he's been forced to chill out down in Hel ever since he got fucked over for being the best in the entire league by that same fucking fire demon who's busy flinging shit all over Beacon Hill[202] right now.

And poor fucking Brady, man! He's sitting this whole fucking battle out due to his suspension by the shit-flinging fire demon, but on the upside he survives even after Goodell sets himself on fire and accidentally burns down the entire fucking universe and then, of course, he goes on to win another Superbowl afterwards! IN FUCKING OVERTIME!!![203]

---

[202] One of Boston's most historic neighborhoods, Beacon Hill is also one of its wealthiest.

[203] This statement is another example of the fluidity of the space-time continuum as conceptualized in the ancient Nordic mindset.

I'm not sure what happens to Gisele…[204]

…Goodell's a fucking prick…

What?

Don't even fucking start with me on this. I swear to fucking God…

I PUT A HOLE IN THE WALL OVER AT THE RINK IN MALDEN!!![205]

Now that was a fucking battle of epic proportions…

My Malden story's fucking poignant and epic as fuck…

…yeah, it's a good story, sometimes it's even kind of fucking poetic, like if Robert Frost were to have gotten ejected for fighting in a men's D league hockey game and started orating *Beowulf* back in the locker room just to let off some steam but then fucking punched the wall anyways…

…well, because sometimes punching the wall is just fucking therapeutic! I bet Robert Frost punched a shit-ton of walls back in his day. And then I bet he went and he mended them like a fucking maniac or some shit, I don't know…

…but yeah, so Odin—who really does love the Pats, by the way—so now he's making his way through Beacon Hill, and he's

---

While *The Impudent Edda*'s recording has been accurately and confidently dated to June 12, 2019, the anonymous poet nonetheless speaks here of grand events that are known to have happened on February 5, 2017 as though they are still yet to happen. It should also be reiterated that the historical record indicates that the poet of *The Impudent Edda* is very inebriated at this stage of his skaldic performance.

[204]   As previously mentioned the myth, *Belichick Rides to Hel*, the anonymous poet seems to be ignorant about Brady's future rebirth in Tampa Bay as well as his subsequent divorce proceedings with Gisele. Even the excessive fluidity of the Old Norse concept of the space-time continuum was clearly unable to assist the poet's knowledge base on these matters.

[205]   Malden, Massachusetts, which derives its name from Maldon, England, is home to one of the Boston area's most heavily used ice rinks for recreational adult hockey.

Norse motif on the Longfellow Bridge, also known as the Salt and Pepper Bridge. The bridge crosses the Charles River from Cambridge to Boston and will provide an appropriate back-drop for the gods when they march towards their impending doom. A Red Line train full of oblivious commuters and students will presumably rumble by at precisely the same moment.

really fucking hoping that Shelley Long's finished up her shift and got out safe and sound[206] before that fucking NFL commissioner showed up and started smearing the bar in human manure, and it's right about now that Thor finally wakes the fuck up from where he's been sleeping it off over at the DD. So he gets his ass up, and he gorges himself on some frozen hash browns since at this point, he's just like, "Who the fuck even cares if they're cold or not?" The world's about to fucking end, and he needs some goddamned

---

206   During the 1980s, Shelley Long was better known as Diane Chambers, the waitress who worked at Cheers, the famous bar where everybody knows your name in the show of the same name.

*Vígríðr, more commonly known as Boston Common, is the
plain at the center of the Hub of the Universe upon which the
final world-shattering battle of Ragnarök will take place.*

nourishment if he's going to go and arm wrestle that piece of shit
Middle-Earth Serpent Snake for once and for all, and so now he's
all carb-loaded up and caffeinated out of his fucking mind, and so
he rushes out over to where the gods and their warriors are preparing to take the field, and he joins up with his old man on the starting line, and together they walk out onto the court at the Public
Garden with Larry Bird, Bill Russell, and John Havlicek since it's
time to beat the fucking shit out of Los Angeles,[207] and so the rest
of the gods, they and their buddies, they all take the field on the

---

[207] This is an oblique reference to the long-standing rivalry between the Boston Celtics and the Los Angeles Lakers.

Common, and then they all just start fucking fighting their rivals, you know? So, like Heimdall and Loki, those two guys basically just kill each other right on the fucking spot, right? And over at the Garden,[208] the Lakers fall to the Celtics in four easy games!

...and uhh...but yeah, you know, so poor fucking Frey, he gets knifed in the back by Goodell, but then Mickey Ward winds up and clocks Goodell right in the fucking face while at the same time Thor finally takes down the serpent, but it sneezes a shit-ton of poison on him which ain't the same as beer, and so Thor can't handle it and he fucking dies, and then Thor's kid, the Green Monster,[209] comes back to life and sprouts some legs and starts rampaging down Boylston Street[210] like a crazy fucking war machine, squashing every evil fucking frost giant that crosses its fucking path! But then the real crazy thing is that, while all this is happening, Odin gets eaten alive by the fucking wolf! I swear to fucking god, that piece of shit canine swallows Odin whole like he's nothing more than a soft fucking wad of peanut butter or something. But then Teddy Williams[211] rises up from out of the Park Street T-Station and rips a homer straight through the wolf's fucking skull...

---

[208]   Not to be confused with the Public Garden, the Boston Garden was a highly esteemed sports venue, and home to the Boston Bruins and Boston Celtics. It no longer exists.

[209]   See the myth, *Thor Begets the Green Monster*, for more on Wally's unique and unusual parentage.

[210]   A busy street in Boston's Back Bay neighborhood that runs near Fenway Park. The Boston Public Library (where Odin passed out drunk in the myth, *Odin Experiments with Public Vagrancy*) also lies alongside Boylston Street.

[211]   *The Prose Edda*'s *Gylfaginning* and *The Poetic Edda*'s *Völuspá* both attribute the slaughter of the wolf to Vidar rather than home-run slugger, Ted Williams. Vidar is Odin's son by the giant-ess, Grid, who in the Elder Eddas is known to have assisted Thor by giving him special equipment when he was en route to visit the giant, Geirrod, which is related in the myth, *Thor Wades through the Menstrual Fluid Fjord*.

...so then, uhhh, okay, so fucking Goodell—who truly, truly fucking hates himself—sets himself on fire when he trips and impales himself on his own fucking sword since no one likes him, and so now that whole fire spreads like a fucking wild fire across the hub, and the entire universe burns to a fucking crisp![212]

Yeah, you know, since we've had such a drought this sum—

Hhuhhh???

...and so yeah, the entire fucking universe burns, and so, of course, all the Nova Scotians are all bawling their fucking eyes out because there just went all their fucking Christmas trees and—

YOU GOT TO BE FUCKING KIDDING ME!!!!

Wha.....???

Uhhhggghhh......

THAT IS FUCKING BULLSHIT!!!!!!!!

---

[212] This fire is equivalent to the final cataclysmic supernova that ends all, or almost all, life in the ancient Norse known universe. The sudden re-ignition of an unknown and unnamed degenerate star by Goodell/Surt's sword causes a chain reaction of nuclear fusion and a subsequent gravitational collapse, ending all life inhabiting the high-energy interstellar structure known as Yggdrasil with only very few exceptions. Yggdrasil itself is subjected to numerous fast-moving shock waves that initiate a new phase of nucleosynthesis that forces the ancient wood of its intergalactic constituent members to groan and strain as it undergoes broad-range endothermic cosmic stress. Yggdrasil survives this cataclysmic event, albeit with a differentiated and new interstellar composition of chemical elements due to the supernova's cosmic ray spallation; its branches have shifted in the cosmic wind, and it has radioactively grown a new, fourth asymptotic giant branch root. The fates of the long-duration gamma ray burst known as Níðhöggr the Dragon and the squirrel-like forbidden mechanism known as Ratatosk have not been specifically addressed by the sources, nor have they yet been adequately studied by scientists. It is thus impossible to comment on their fate at the time of this printing.

Jesus Christ...HOW THE FUCK?!?
Ugh...[213]

---

[213]   At this point in the recording, *The Impudent Edda* deterio-
rates into a series of incoherent gurgles and expletives about the
goaltending of Tuuka Rask and the "douchebaggery" of the St.
Louis Blues. As with many historical manuscripts, the incom-
pleteness leaves us only with the ability to speculate about the
missing material, and we will never know exactly how the anonymous poet intended to formally end his Edda. We can at least
attempt to fill the void with the knowledge that has been retained
in the Elder Eddas, and thereby postulate a probable conclusion
to the events thus far described. Despite numerous deviations,
omissions, and new fabrications, *The Impudent Edda* has throughout its course generally followed the same mythological story arc
as the Elder Eddas, so it remains likely that it would have continued along this same trajectory, describing the same or similar
events and outcomes, though perhaps with some deviations.
      The inferno started by Surt (or Goodell, in *The Impudent Ed-
da*'s version) rages throughout all the 9 Worlds, burning and killing all. Or almost all. As the flames eventually subside, it comes
to be revealed that there are, in fact, a limited number of survi-
vors. Among these are Odin's sons, Vidar and Vali, and Thor's
sons, Modi and Magni. Odin's previously dead sons, Brady/Bald-
er and Hod, will survive and return from the depths of Hel where
they sat out the final battle between gods and monsters. Odin's
brothers, Vili and Ve, will also survive, as will Hoenir, who had
been sent to live among the Vanir as part of the two tribes of
gods' truce agreement in the early days following the war that
was instigated when Odin murdered a witch. Two humans who
hid deep in the branches and bark of Yggdrasil will also survive
the universe cleansing-flames, and they will repopulate the world.
The sun will be reborn, and the world will grow good and green
and new all over again.
      The fact that the Elder Eddas contain a world-rebirth myth
and that *The Impudent Edda* does not can only lead one to con-
template that present-day Boston sports fans are perhaps even
more fatalistic than the ancient Scandinavians had been.

Concluding Remarks

The recording of *The Impudent Edda* ends in a downward spiral of drunken stupor, characterized by increasingly frequent deviations from its description of Ragnarök in favor of hostile invectives that deride the cohesive teamwork and frustratingly superior play of the 2019 Stanley Cup Finals Game 7 winners, the St. Louis Blues. After a final sequence of eloquently timed F-bombs, curses about the goaltending of Tuuka Rask in the final minutes of the game, and expressions of general disgust and a desire to go home, the unknown orator then asks the name of his equally unknown drinking partner, whom he has presumably never previously met (and who may very well have been an unwilling recipient of the archaic knowledge revealed), and then the recording abruptly ends, the electronic device having reached the full extent of its available hard-disc space. We can only speculate as to how the electronic device containing this invaluable trove of Norse lore ended up in the dark corner of a dank alleyway that appears to only ever be frequented by late-night inebriated patrons of local neighborhood drinking establishments when in desperate need of relieving their full and aching bladders.

In the course of its telling, *The Impudent Edda* corroborates many details found in the Elder Eddas and provides many new and heretofore unknown details that have expanded our knowledge of ancient Scandinavian mythological beliefs. Stories such as those about Thor's fathering of the Green Monster or Odin's passing out shit-faced on the steps of the Boston Public Library have granted us new insight into the world that the Norse gods inhabit. They have also increased our understanding of the sorts of behavioral characteristics and interactions with which the gods engage one another. Generally, these new revelations remain consistent with and support the characteristics of the gods that have been propagated by the Elder Eddas for centuries.

While *The Impudent Edda* has strengthened our knowledge concerning many ancient stories of the Norse gods and contributed a few new ones, it has also completely neglected some of the most prominent stories described in the earlier sources. *The Impudent Edda* offers no new knowledge, for example, about the story of Thor's journey to Giant Land in which he attempts to display feats of strength and drinking prowess but is instead made to look like a fool, or about his battle with the evil giant, Hrungnir, in which he emerges the obvious victor but with a piece of a whetstone lodged eternally in his head forever after, or about Loki's "flyting," in which Loki hurls insults at each and every one of the gods and goddesses after the death of Brady/Balder and immediately prior his subsequent capture and torture. This myth, contained within the *Lokasenna* in *The Poetic Edda*, plays a particularly pivotal role in advancing the narrative towards Ragnarök, but goes essentially unobserved in both *The Prose Edda* and *The Impudent Edda*.

None of which is entirely surprising, since by nature, mythology has always been ever-evolving and never 100% consistent. We have long thought Norse mythology to be stuck in a state of stasis ever since the conversion of the Northlands to Christianity in the medieval period, but now we have reason and sufficient literary evidence to believe that this may never have actually been the case. The stories of the dread god, Odin, his boisterous son, Thor, and all the others have lived on, not only in the most popular forms of pop culture (albeit with varying degrees of substance and genuineness) such as those evidenced by the comics/films of Marvel or the novels of Neil Gaiman, but also in terms of the actual religious beliefs that adhere to and further shape the lives and behaviors of the gods.

With the rise of contemporary Ásatrú and its increasing acceptance by larger swaths of society, we may again, perhaps even someday soon, greet another revolutionary breakthrough in our collective knowledge of Norse mythology. But until the next great discovery is made, let us rest with some degree of contentment with the new, invaluable knowledge that *The Impudent Edda* has bestowed upon us.

—ROWDY GEIRSSON

Appendix:
The Lay of the Bs

While not a traditional myth in the typical sense, the Impudent Eddic segment known as *The Lay of the Bs* nonetheless constitutes original *Codex Bostonia* literary material. Unlike the side notes, misinterpretations, and various fabrications added by medieval and early modern scribes in the process of creating copies of original manuscripts, *The Lay of the Bs* is genuine to its original recording. The segment takes the form of a pointless digression between the myths about Thor's failed evil serpent fishing trip and his subsequent experience with giantess menstrual fluid; apparently the anonymous poet of *The Impudent Edda* thought that his listener(s) needed to know about the Boston Bruins (nicknamed in their home town as the 'Bs') and their 2011 Stanley Cup Championship.

Furthermore, it is interesting to note that *The Lay of the Bs*—and the entirety of *The Impudent Edda* for that matter—was recorded during Game 7 of the 2019 Stanley Cup Finals in which the Boston Bruins suffered a disappointing and heart-breaking defeat to a midwestern hockey team symbolized by a lame music note. Given the anonymous poet's extreme devotion to Odin's team, one wonders what elaborate verses and ornate turns of phrase he might have constructed to describe the Bruins' record-breaking 2022-2023 regular season performance and their subsequent, humiliating elimination during the first round of the 2023 NHL Playoffs. Sadly, we will never know.

Despite its general uselessness, *The Lay of the Bs* nonetheless features a format that frequently occurs in Old Norse literature: the thula, which is essentially a listing of names of a certain

Created by artist, Harry Weber, and available for public viewing on hallowed ground that was once home to the hall of legends, the Boston Garden, this statue depicts the local god of offensive defense and victory on ice, Bobby Orr, flying through the air after scoring the Stanley Cup winning goal in 1970 over the forces of evil as embodied by the St. Louis Blues. Perhaps an ominous portent considering the date and circumstances during which The Impudent Edda *was recorded.*

class, group, or family of people or other beings or creatures. As with *The Lay of the Bs* itself, these ancient digressions are also commonly embedded within the text of the actual myth or saga itself, and while succinctly and curtly imparting the knowledge of who's-who's and what's-what's that the narrator clearly has deemed important, they also often break the flow of the overall narrative. A particularly well-known example may be found in the *Völuspá* of *The Poetic Edda*. Known as the *Dvergatal* ("*Catalogue of Dwarves*"), which comprises stanzas 9-16 of the *Völuspá*, it recounts the names of famous dwarves from Norse mythology, and anyone familiar with the mythological English works of Tolkien will recognize many of them. *The Lay of the Bs* simply continues this long and tedious tradition.

THE LAY OF THE Bs

Shit dude, fucking 2011 Stanley Cup champions, man!

So, of course, there was Chara the Captain, that fucking Slovakian giant and, naturally, Lucic the fucking fighter and Bergeron and Marchand and Krejci leading the forwards with their wicked good stickhandling.

Then you got guys like Johnny Boychuk and Dennis Seidenberg backing up the blue line with Bartkowski, Ference, and McQuaid and Rask in goal making poor Tim Thomas feel like Bledsoe.

Savard and pretty boy Seguin, Horton and Chris Kelly working it in deep in the offensive zone.

Mark Recchi who's still going strong after all these years.

I also remember Campbell, Ryder, and Wheeler. And Shawn Thornton was there, too.

And so were Peverley, Hunwick, Caron, and Stuart.

And, of course, Paille! Who can fucking forget Paille? And Kampfer and Kaberle. And guys like Arniel, Hamill, and Hnidy who didn't get much ice time but were still a part of the squad.

These are the guys I remember most, and who fucking deserved to have their names etched onto Lord Stanley's Cup, the one and the only, so that the world would never ever forget how awesome they played that year.

Acknowledgements

Translating a literary work from a semi-foreign language to English is always a solitary task, and one that will probably be automated by AI in the near future, ultimately eliminating the livelihoods of many people across many professions as the world takes one giant leap closer towards becoming the godforsaken Hellscape that it is destined to become. But be that as it may, we're not quite there just yet at the time of this writing, and so I'd like to thank a few people who made the journey of translating this Edda possible and supported it along the way.

First and foremost, I'd like to thank the anonymous poet himself, wherever he may be. Without his masterful skaldic performance, our knowledge of ancient Scandinavian religious beliefs today would be greatly diminished. So, thank you, Drunken Anonymous Boston Skald, wherever you may be (hopefully, not down in Hel, sitting beside Charlie and Brady).

I'd also like to thank Snorri Sturluson and Saemundr Sigfusson (or whoever it was that compiled *The Prose Edda*). Without their major contributions in medieval Iceland, the third Edda would never have surfaced as a fitting conclusion to *The Edda Trilogy*.

A special, heartfelt thanks to the Boston Bruins, the Boston Celtics, the Boston Red Sox, and the New England Patriots.

Another special, heartfelt thanks to Samuel Adams (the man and the beer), The Dropkick Murphys, *Good Will Hunting*, Roisin Dubh, the Boston Tea Party, *The Departed*, the New England Senior Hockey League and its associated worn-out ice rinks scattered around eastern Massachusetts, Dunkin' Donuts, the

Pilgrims, clam chowder (not that filthy Manhattan shit), Charlie's exit fare, the Green Monster, the Harvard Bookstore, Lenny Clarke, the Freedom Trail, the MBTA (the good, the bad, and the ugly of it), the Big Dig and its multi-decade comedy of errors, *More Than a Feeling*, Erikson's Ice Cream out in Maynard, Idle Hands Craft Ales, Eben Norton Horsford, fresh buttered lobster meat, the Norumbega tower, Paul Revere and his midnight ride, Wayne's hammer, Armageddon Record Shop, Grendel's Den, Eddie Coyle and his friends, Frederick Law Olmstead, Norm Peterson and Cliff Clavin, Aerosmith, and, last but most definitely not least, Mark "Funky Bunch" Wahlberg.

Thanks to Chris Monks for being the first (way back in 2010) to believe in the educational value of my transcriptions of ancient Scandinavian history and mythological lore and for providing happy evidence that the monastic disciples of dominant cultural trends and crosscurrent literary heathens can get along despite all the historic evidence to the contrary.

A special thank you to Bjørn Larssen for suggesting the notion that an actual translation, and not just a simple transcription, of *The Impudent Edda* might be a worthwhile endeavor, and for encouraging its slow and steady gestation. For those of you who are reading this: do yourself a favor and go acquire a copy of his book, *Why Odin Drinks*, if you like funny Norse things, or *Children*, if you like grim Norse things. Or better yet, go acquire a copy of both.

Finally, some special shout-outs to other Eddic supporters over the years: my parents and sister, Doomsday Mike, Corwin the figurative son of Eric, Pearse and Bev and Bob of Boston Accent podcast notoriety, Dave and Lynn of Ichabod and Eir's Garden (respectively) and Navigation Brewing (collectively), and, last but certainly not least, everyone else who has just so happened to pick up a copy of this lore-drenched tome and given the old gods the undivided attention they so richly deserve.

Image Credits

PAGE xi
Alleyway in South Boston
Photo by Rowdy Geirsson, 2019

PAGE xiii
Odin (18th Century Icelandic Illustration)
Stofnun Árna Magnússonar á Íslandi (SÁM) 66, page 77
Courtesy of the Árni Magnússon Institute for Icelandic Studies
https://handrit.is/en/manuscript/view/is/SAM-0066
Photo Alteration by Rowdy Geirsson, 2019

PAGE xv
Kensington Runestone
Photo provided by the Runestone Museum Foundation
https://runestonemuseum.org/

PAGE xxv
The Ash Yggdrasil
Illustration by Friedrich Wilhelm Heine, 1886
Public Domain
*https://commons.wikimedia.org/wiki/File:The_Ash_Yggdrasil_by_*
Friedrich_Wilhelm_Heine.jpg

PAGE 9
Revere Beach
Photo by Rowdy Geirsson, 2019

PAGE 15
Statyett (Odenfigur) av brons
SHM Object Identification #109043
Photo by Gabriel Hildebrand, 2011
Historiska Museet Stockholm
Reprinted in accordance with CC BY 2.5 SE
https://historiska.se/upptack-historien/object/109043-statyett-odenfigur-av-brons/

PAGE 21
Bird at San Francisco Bay
Photo by Rowdy Geirsson, 2008

PAGE 25
Kam (enkelkam, a3) av ben/horn
SHM Object Identification #269167
Photo by Christer Åhlin, 2011
Historiska Museet Stockholm
Reprinted in accordance with CC BY 2.5 SE
https://historiska.se/upptack-historien/object/269167-kam-enkelkam-a3-av-ben-horn/

PAGE 28
Bethel Saloon/ Dwarf MC Clubhouse
Photo by Nomadic Lana, 2007
Adapted by Rowdy Geirsson, 2023
Reprinted in accordance with CC BY 2.0
https://www.flickr.com/photos/lanacar/422792886

PAGE 30
Sövestad-runesten (Krageholm)
Photo by Erik Moltke, 1939
Nationalmuseet Danmark
Reprinted in accordance with CC BY SA 2.0
https://samlinger.natmus.dk/DMR/asset/5752

PAGE 33
Agassiz Road Duck House
Photo by Rowdy Geirsson, 2019

PAGE 34
Lansdowne Street
Photo by Rowdy Geirsson, 2019

PAGE 41
Leonard P. Zakim Bunker Hill Memorial Bridge
Photo by Rowdy Geirsson, 2019

PAGE 46
Det længste guldhorn fra Gallehus (kopi)
Object Identification #18964
Photo by Roberto Fortuna and Kira Ursem, 2007
Nationalmuseet Danmark
Reprinted in accordance with CC BY SA 2.0
https://samlinger.natmus.dk/DO/asset/2869

PAGE 51
Observatory Tower in Rime with Blue Sky
Photo by Michael Davidson, 2004
Reprinted in accordance with CC BY SA 3.0
https://commons.wikimedia.org/wiki/File:Observatory_tower_in_rime_with_blue_sky.jpg

PAGE 55
Hänge (freja) av silver
SHM Object Identification #107873
Photo by Gabriel Hildebrand, 2011
Historiska Museet Stockholm
Reprinted in accordance with CC BY 2.5 SE
https://historiska.se/upptack-historien/object/107873-hange-freja-av-silver/

PAGE 59
Urban Turkey in a New England Street Gutter
Photo by Rowdy Geirsson, 2023

PAGE 62
White Mountain National Forest
Photo by Rowdy Geirsson, 2019

PAGE 94
Statyett (statyett av frö) av brons
SHM Object Identification #109037
Photo by Gabriel Hildebrand, 2011
Historiska Museet Stockholm
Reprinted in accordance with CC BY 2.5 SE
*https://historiska.se/upptack-historien/object/109037-
statyett-statyett-av-fro-av-brons/*

PAGE 98
Parking Garage in Boston
Photo by Rowdy Geirsson, 2019

PAGE 105
Dyrehoved, ukendt findested
Object Identification #C31157
Photo by John Lee, 2005
Nationalmuseet Danmark
Reprinted in accordance with CC BY SA 2.0
https://samlinger.natmus.dk/DO/asset/1606

PAGE 110
Pumpkin Tower in Keene, NH
Photo by Rowdy Geirsson, 2004

PAGE 113
Original Filene's and Filene's Basement Location
Photo by Rowdy Geirsson, 2019

PAGE 117
Gårastolen
Photo by Andreas Harvik and Annar Bjørgli, 2021
Nasjonalmuseet
Reprinted in accordance with CC BY 4.0
https://www.nasjonalmuseet.no/samlingen/objekt/OK-10700

PAGE 120
New England Aquarium
Photo by Rowdy Geirsson, 2019

PAGE 126
Carving, Oosik
Object Identification #UAM:EH:UA99-018-0115
Courtesty of University of Alaska Museum of the North
Photo by Mahriena Ellanna
http://arctos.database.museum/guid/UAM:EH:UA99-018-0115

PAGE 128
New Hampshire Liquor and Wine Outlet
Photo by Rowdy Geirsson, 2023

PAGE 134
Tjängvidestenen
SHM Object Identification #108203
Photo by Ola Myrin, 2017
Historiska Museet Stockholm
Reprinted in accordance with CC BY 2.5 SE
http://mis.historiska.se/mis/sok/bild.asp?uid=446023

PAGE 137
Charlie Poster at the Harvard Square T-Station
Photo by Rowdy Geirsson, 2023

PAGE 140
New England River Rapids
Photo by Rowdy Geirsson, 2019

PAGE 146
New England Holocaust Memorial
Photo by Rowdy Geirsson, 2019

PAGE 148
Union Oyster House
Photo by Carol Highsmith, 1980
Reprinted in accordance with CC Public Domain Mark 1.0
https://picryl.com/media/famous-union-oyster-house-boston-massa-chusetts

PAGE 151
Dunkin' Donuts in Downtown Boston
Photo by Rowdy Geirsson, 2019

PAGE 155
Charles Street Manholes
Photo by Rowdy Geirsson, 2019

PAGE 157
The Asgard Bar Sign
Photo by Rowdy Geirsson, 2021

PAGE 159
Longfellow Bridge
Photo by Rowdy Geirsson, 2019

PAGE 160
Boston Common
Photo by Rowdy Geirsson, 2019

PAGE 170
Bobby Orr Statue
Photo by Rowdy Geirsson, 2019

Index

NORSE MYTHOLOGY FOR BOSTONIANS

McSweeney's Internet Tendency
NORSE MYTHOLOGY FOR BOSTONIANS
ROWDY GEIRSSON

In 2019 an abandoned smartphone was found partially buried beneath layers of sediment and urine in a South Boston alleyway. This forgotten relic was soon revealed to contain a remarkable audio-text describing in great detail the religious beliefs of ancient Scandinavia. The oral manuscript found on this device was transcribed and released to the general public as *Norse Mythology for Bostonians* in early 2020, and subsequently translated and released to the public as *The Impudent Edda*—the very book that you now hold in your hands, dear reader.

Archaeologists, historians, and philologists have continued to study the audio text as well as the device itself, now known simply as the *Codex Bostonia*. These researchers eventually uncovered an additional stash of hidden audio files stored in a previously secret location on the phone's memory card. Since the fall of 2022, these recently recovered myths are being made available to the public at McSweeney's on a rolling basis as they are uncovered.

The breadth of these lost myths' arcane lore, the depth of their spiritual insights, and the poignancy of their poetic revelations confirm that the collective audio texts of the *Codex Bostonia* remain the single most important contribution to our knowledge of pre-Christian Scandinavian religious beliefs to have emerged in a millennium.

NORSE MYTHOLOGY FOR BOSTONIANS

Illustration from the uncovered lost myth, *Thor and Loki Go Christmas Shopping* (first released to the public in December of 2022), by Matt Smith

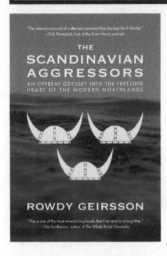

"HE IS HARD TO GET ALONG WITH."

Equal parts Egil Skallagrimsson and Thundarr the Barbarian, Barbarian Lord is a character borne of the unvarnished tone of the medieval Icelandic Sagas with a heavy infusion of 1980's barbarian cartoons. 176 pages of grim determination may be enjoyed with the noble brute via the *Barbarian Lord* graphic novel, released by Clarion Books.